Chapter and Unit Tests
English Language Learners
and Special-Needs Students
with Answer Key

HOLT

Civics

HOLT, RINEHART AND WINSTON

A Harcourt Education Company

Austin • Orlando • Chicago • New York • Toronto • London • San Diego

Printed in the United States of America

ISBN 0-03-038718-3
1 2 3 4 5 6 7 8 9 082 07 06 05 04

Contents

Chapter and Unit Tests for English Language Learners and Special-Needs Students

Name _____ Class _____ Date _____

 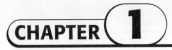
Chapter Test Form C

We the People

MATCHING *(3 points each)* Place the letters of the descriptions next to the appropriate terms.

_____ **1.** government

_____ **2.** deport

_____ **3.** quota

_____ **4.** census

_____ **5.** urban areas

_____ **6.** civics

_____ **7.** naturalization

_____ **8.** metropolitan areas

_____ **9.** refugees

_____ **10.** citizen

a. the legal process by which an alien may become a citizen

b. a legally recognized member of a country

c. people fleeing persecution in their home countries

d. areas made up of cities and their suburbs

e. set numbers

f. to force to leave the country

g. the study of what it means to be a U.S. citizen

h. used to find out the size of a state's population

i. the organizations, institutions, and individuals who exercise authority as a political unit over a group of people

j. cities

FILL IN THE BLANK *(3 points each)* Choose from the following list to complete each of the statements below.

immigrant   death rate   heritage   metropolitan areas
quotas   native-born citizen   citizen
birthrate   Sunbelt   resources

1. A(n) _____ is a person who came to the United States from other lands.

2. If you are born in any U.S. state or territory, you automatically become a(n)

_____ .

3. A(n) _____ is a legally recognized member of a country.

4. The United States used to set _____ on how many immigrants could come into the country.

5. We must use our natural _____ wisely.

6. More than four fifths of the current U.S. population lives in

_____ , or areas made up of cities and their suburbs.

7. The states in the South and West are known as the _____.

8. The United States has a(n) _____ of liberty and freedom.

TRUE/FALSE *(2 points each)* Mark each statement *T* if it is true or *F* if it is false.

_____ **1.** Under the U.S. form of government, the people rule through the officials they elect.

_____ **2.** It is not the responsibility of state and local governments to provide free public schools for all young citizens.

_____ **3.** The study of civics helps you learn your role in government.

_____ **4.** Many Africans were brought to the Americas as slaves.

_____ **5.** The government cannot force aliens to leave the United States, even if they violate a law.

_____ **6.** In order to be naturalized, aliens must prove that they can read, write, and speak English.

_____ **7.** Countries grow in only one way—when the birthrate is greater than the death rate.

_____ **8.** People believe that although the population itself will increase in the future, the rate of increase will drop.

_____ **9.** Hispanics are the largest minority group in the United States.

_____ **10.** Many couples in the United States are having fewer children.

_____ **11.** The census not only tells us the size of each state's population but also can tell us about the people who live in the United States.

_____ **12.** Officials cannot be removed from office once they are elected by the people.

_____ **13.** Aliens may vote, but they cannot hold public office.

_____ **14.** In the past, many people moved from urban to rural areas.

IDENTIFICATION *(3 points each)* Insert the letter of the correct description into its proper place on the flowchart.

a. Immigrant has a background check.

b. Immigrant appears at an interview to show good moral character and prove knowledge of English.

c. Immigrant may file a declaration of intention.

d. Immigrant receives a date for an interview with a naturalization official.

e. Immigrant fills out a petition for naturalization.

f. Immigrant takes an oath of allegiance to the United States.

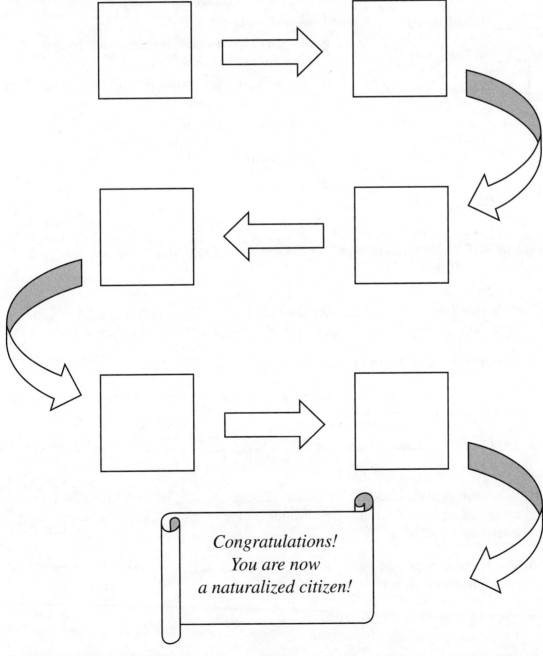

Congratulations!
You are now
a naturalized citizen!

CHAPTER **2** — Chapter Test Form C

Foundations of Government

MATCHING *(3 points each)* Write the letters of the descriptions next to the appropriate terms.

_____ **1.** monarchies

_____ **2.** democracy

_____ **3.** direct democracy

_____ **4.** constitution

_____ **5.** Parliament

_____ **6.** Federalists

_____ **7.** delegates

_____ **8.** representative democracy

_____ **9.** legislature

_____ **10.** bicameral

a. the lawmaking body of Great Britain

b. the people elect representatives to carry on the work of government for them

c. consisting of two parts

d. a written plan of government

e. governments controlled by kings or queens

f. lawmaking body

g. all voters in a community meet in one place to make laws and decide what actions to take

h. supporters of the Constitution who wanted a strong national government

i. allows the people of the country to either rule directly or elect officials who act on their behalf

j. representatives

FILL IN THE BLANK *(3 points each)* Choose from the following list to complete each of the statements below.

unitary system	totalitarian	republic
Antifederalists	dictatorship	ratification
Federalism	laws	compromise

1. Rules of conduct for a group are called _____.

2. _____ divides a government's powers between the national government and state governments.

3. The Constitution had to be sent to the states for _____, or approval.

4. Dictatorships are considered _____ when the ruler attempts to control all aspects of citizens' lives, including their religious, cultural, political, and even personal activities.

5. The delegates eventually had to _____, and each side gave up a part of its demands in order to reach a solution.

6. The United States is considered a(n) _____.

Chapter 2, Test Form C, continued

7. The type of government in which the ruler has absolute control over the government

is a(n) _____.

8. In a(n) _____, the national government possesses all legal
power.

9. People who opposed the new Constitution and did not want a strong national gov-

ernment were called _____.

TRUE/FALSE *(2 points each)* Mark each statement *T* if it is true or *F* if it is false.

_____ **1.** In most countries that have monarchs, the monarchs' power is greatly limited.

_____ **2.** The U.S. government provides its citizens with a system of money, trash
collection, and highways.

_____ **3.** The Declaration of Independence was approved by members of the
Continental Congress on July 4, 1776.

_____ **4.** The Articles of Confederation were approved by only 10 states.

_____ **5.** Under the Articles of Confederation, Congress had the power to force states
to pay taxes.

_____ **6.** The majority of people in the 13 states wanted a strong central government.

_____ **7.** George Washington was chosen to preside over the Constitutional
Convention.

_____ **8.** Only two states, North Carolina and Rhode Island, did not approve the
Constitution until after it went into effect.

_____ **9.** Every country in the world has the same type of government.

_____ **10.** The Articles of Confederation gave more power to the states and less to the
national government.

_____ **11.** Only some individuals have the right to life, liberty, and the pursuit of
happiness, according to the Declaration of Independence.

_____ **12.** Constitutional Convention meetings were secret.

_____ **13.** In the Senate, states have equal representation. In the House of
Representatives, each state is represented according to population.

_____ **14.** By the time the Constitution was completed, every delegate was satisfied with
every part of the document.

Name _____ Class _____ Date _____

IDENTIFICATION *(3 points each)* Write the letter of the correct description in the proper place on the time line.

   a. Articles of Confederation are approved, setting up a plan of government.
   b. Declaration of Independence is approved by Continental Congress.
   c. George Washington becomes president of the new nation.
   d. Constitution is ratified by most states.
   e. Constitutional Convention meets.

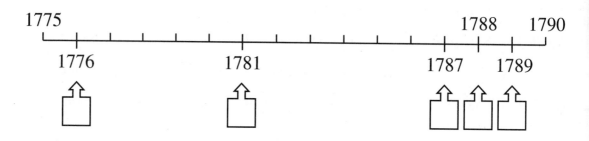

Name _____ Class _____ Date _____

Chapter Test Form C

The U.S. Constitution

MATCHING *(3 points each)* Place the letters of the descriptions next to the appropriate terms.

_____ **1.** popular sovereignty

_____ **2.** majority rule

_____ **3.** concurrent powers

_____ **4.** Preamble

_____ **5.** legislative branch

_____ **6.** judicial branch

_____ **7.** checks and balances

_____ **8.** veto

_____ **9.** amendment

_____ **10.** repeal

a. lawmaking branch of government

b. a written change made to the Constitution

c. consent of the governed

d. system in which powers of each branch of government are limited by those of the other two branches

e. the opening sentence of the Constitution

f. to cancel

g. principle that ensures that when people disagree, everyone accepts the decision of the majority

h. to turn down

i. powers shared by both the federal and state governments

j. branch of government that interprets laws and punishes lawbreakers

FILL IN THE BLANK *(3 points each)* Choose from the following list to complete each of the statements below.

delegated powers   veto   Preamble
limited government   reserved powers
popular sovereignty   majority rule

1. Our government is a _____, meaning that there are certain checks on its power.

2. The U.S. government is based on _____, meaning it follows the will of most of the people.

3. The powers that the Constitution specifically gives to the federal government are

called _____.

4. The opening sentence of the Constitution is the _____; it explains why the U.S. Constitution was written.

5. _____ means the consent of the governed.

6. The powers that are set aside for the states or the people are called

_____.

Chapter 3, Test Form C, continued

TRUE/FALSE *(2 points each)* Mark each statement *T* if it is true or *F* if it is false.

_____ **1.** If U.S. citizens become dissatisfied with the way their representatives are governing, there is nothing they can do.

_____ **2.** The U.S. system of government is based in part on Magna Carta.

_____ **3.** The framers of the Constitution wanted to emphasize the importance of the people.

_____ **4.** The judicial branch has the most power of all three branches.

_____ **5.** The executive branch includes the president and vice president.

_____ **6.** The executive branch is made up of two houses—the Senate and the House of Representatives.

_____ **7.** Only the president needs to approve an amendment for it to be written into the Constitution.

_____ **8.** Unfortunately, the Constitution is not very flexible.

_____ **9.** The president meets regularly with his cabinet.

_____ **10.** The framers of the Constitution believed that they could foresee all of the changes the United States would undergo.

_____ **11.** The Preamble begins with the words "We the people."

_____ **12.** A representative democracy may also be called a republic.

_____ **13.** By establishing the federal system, the framers of the Constitution set up a weaker national government than the new nation needed.

_____ **14.** Our republic is based upon the idea of minority rule.

Name _____ Class _____ Date _____

IDENTIFICATION *(3 points each)* Complete the graphic organizer below by filling in the branch of government along with the correct description of its power.

legislative branch

judicial branch

carries out laws

makes laws

executive branch

interprets laws and punishes lawbreakers

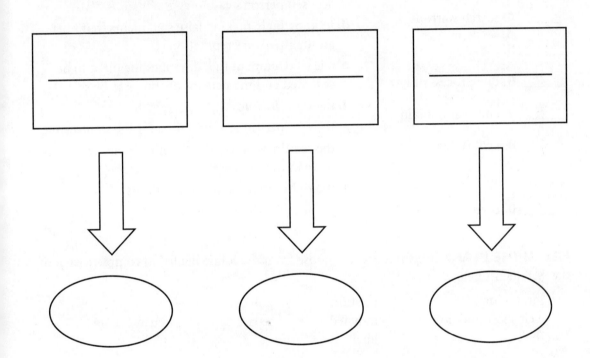

CHAPTER  4

Chapter Test Form C
Rights and Responsibilities

MATCHING *(3 points each)* Place the letters of the descriptions next to the appropriate terms.

_____ **1.** double jeopardy

_____ **2.** slander

_____ **3.** petition

_____ **4.** search warrant

_____ **5.** indict

_____ **6.** due process of law

_____ **7.** eminent domain

_____ **8.** civil rights

_____ **9.** suffrage

_____ **10.** draft

a. a formal request

b. the government's power to take citizens' private property for public use

c. the just and fair application of the law to an accused person's case

d. to knowingly making false statements that hurt another person's reputation

e. a legal document that describes the place to be searched and the persons or things to be seized

f. the right to vote

g. trying a person a second time for the same crime

h. the requirement of men meeting qualifications to serve in the military

i. the rights guaranteed to all citizens

j. to formally accuse of a crime

FILL IN THE BLANK *(3 points each)* Choose from the following list to complete each of the statements below.

grand jury   petition   poll tax
self-incrimination   indicted   separation of church and state
bail   libel

1. Courts have decided to prevent people from holding prayers in public schools because of the _____.

2. If a member of the press prints statements that are untrue and hurt another person's reputation, he or she may be sued for _____.

3. The Fifth Amendment protects an accused person against

_____, or having to testify against oneself.

4. The money or property an accused person gives a court to hold as a guarantee that he or she will appear for trial is _____.

5. Many Americans believed that the _____ was aimed at preventing poor people from voting.

Chapter 4, Test Form C, continued

6. A(n) _____ decides if there is enough evidence against a person to go to trial.

7. If you wanted the government to change something, you might ask people to help you create a(n) _____.

8. A person may go to trial, but he or she must first be _____, or formally accused.

TRUE/FALSE *(2 points each)* Mark each statement *T* if it is true or *F* if it is false.

_____ **1.** The Second Amendment protects the right to bear arms.

_____ **2.** Freedom of the press allows Americans the right to express their thoughts freely in writing. However, they must not state falsehoods that ruin a person's reputation.

_____ **3.** The Thirteenth Amendment not only outlawed slavery but also gave African Americans the right to vote.

_____ **4.** Before the Twenty-third Amendment, people living in Washington, D.C., could not vote in national elections.

_____ **5.** Many people believed that the poll tax was meant to prevent poor people from voting.

_____ **6.** Upon turning 21, all men must register for the draft.

_____ **7.** As an American citizen, if you are called to be a member of a jury, you have the option of refusing.

_____ **8.** All citizens are required to serve as government officials.

_____ **9.** Public schools guarantee only some young people the opportunity to be educated.

_____ **10.** The government can search people's property for any reason any time it wants.

_____ **11.** As an American, you only need to pay taxes if you agree with what the government is doing.

Chapter 4, Test Form C, continued

IDENTIFICATION *(2 points each)* Complete the table by writing the items below in the appropriate places.

Fourteenth Amendment
guarantees freedom of religion, speech, and the press
forbids the use of a poll tax
Nineteenth Amendment
Third Amendment
grants eligible voters in a state the right to elect the state's U.S. senators

guarantees the right to bear arms
grants African Americans the right to vote
grants people living in Washington, D.C., the right to vote in national elections
provides trial by jury in cases that involve conflicts over money or property
outlaws slavery
lowers voting age to 18

Amendment	What the Amendment Does
First	1.
Second	2.
3.	Government cannot quarter soldiers in private citizens' homes during peacetime without the owners' consent.
Seventh	4.
Thirteenth	5.
6.	Grants full citizenship to African Americans
Fifteenth	7.
Seventeenth	8.
9.	Women are granted the right to vote.
Twenty-third	10.
Twenty-fourth	11.
Twenty-sixth	12.

UNIT 1

Unit Test Form C

A Tradition of Democracy

MATCHING *(3 points each)* Place the letters of the descriptions next to the appropriate terms.

_____ **1.** quota

_____ **2.** monarchies

_____ **3.** legislative branch

_____ **4.** representative democracy

_____ **5.** bicameral

_____ **6.** popular sovereignty

_____ **7.** naturalization

_____ **8.** judicial branch

_____ **9.** suffrage

_____ **10.** civics

_____ **11.** amendment

_____ **12.** due process of law

a. written change to the Constitution

b. the legal process by which an alien may become a citizen

c. branch of government that interprets laws and punishes lawbreakers

d. consent of the governed

e. set numbers

f. the right to vote

g. The people elect representatives to carry on the work of government for them.

h. the study of what it means to be a U.S. citizen

i. governments controlled by kings or queens

j. the branch of government that makes the laws

k. consisting of two parts

l. A person can be punished for a crime only after the law has been justly and fairly applied to his or her case.

FILL IN THE BLANK *(3 points each)* Choose from the following list to complete each of the statements below.

native-born citizen   republic   Antifederalists
self-incrimination   limited government   immigrant
totalitarian   delegated powers   libel

1. A _____ government attempts to control all aspects of citizens' lives, including their religious, cultural, political, and even personal activities.

2. The powers that the Constitution specifically gives to the federal government are

called _____.

Unit 1, Chapter Test Form C, continued

3. If you are born in any U.S. state or territory, you automatically become a(n)

_____.

4. People who opposed the new Constitution and did not want a strong national government were called _____.

5. The United States is considered a(n) _____.

6. A(n) _____ is a person who came to the United States from another land.

7. Our government is a(n) _____, meaning that there are certain limitations to its power.

8. The Fifth Amendment protects an accused person against _____,

or having to testify against oneself.

9. If a member of the press prints statements that are not true and hurt another

person's reputation, he or she may be sued for _____.

TRUE/FALSE *(2 points each)* Mark each statement *T* if it is true or *F* if it is false.

_____ **1.** It is not the responsibility of state and local governments to provide free public schools for all young citizens.

_____ **2.** The U.S. government provides its citizens with a system of money, trash collection, and highways.

_____ **3.** Freedom of the press allows Americans the right to express their thoughts freely in writing. However, they must not state falsehoods that ruin a person's reputation.

_____ **4.** The Articles of Confederation gave more power to the states and less to the national government.

_____ **5.** The executive branch is made up of two houses—the Senate and the House of Representatives.

_____ **6.** Unfortunately, the Constitution is not very flexible.

_____ **7.** Hispanics are the largest minority group in the United States.

_____ **8.** In order to be naturalized, aliens must prove that they can read, write, and speak English.

Unit 1, Chapter Test Form C, continued

IDENTIFICATION *(3 points each)* Place the letter of the description into the correct box.

  a. Nineteenth Amendment guarantees women the right to vote.

  b. George Washington becomes president of the new country.

  c. Fifteenth Amendment guarantees African Americans the right to vote.

  d. Declaration of Independence is approved by the Continental Congress.

  e. Thirteenth Amendment is ratified, outlawing slavery.

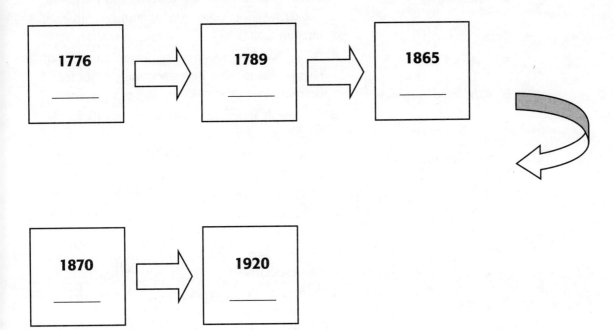

CHAPTER **5**   Chapter Test Form C

The Legislative Branch

MATCHING *(3 points each)* Place the letters of the descriptions next to the appropriate terms.

_____ **1.** gerrymandering

_____ **2.** constituents

_____ **3.** caucuses

_____ **4.** Speaker

_____ **5.** party whip

_____ **6.** standing committees

_____ **7.** implied powers

_____ **8.** bill of attainder

_____ **9.** quorum

_____ **10.** elastic clause

a. permanent committees

b. assists floor leaders in trying to persuade members to vote for party-sponsored legislation

c. private meetings of Republicans and Democrats occurring shortly after the opening day of each term of Congress

d. states that Congress has the power "to make all laws which shall be necessary and proper for carrying into execution the foregoing powers"

e. the people who live in a congressmember's home district or state

f. state legislatures' practice of drawing distinct district lines that favor a particular political party, politician, or group of people

g. a law that sentences a person to prison without a trial

h. the presiding officer of the House of Representatives

i. powers that Congress claims under the elastic clause

j. a majority of the members

FILL IN THE BLANK *(3 points each)* Choose from the following list to complete each of the statements below.

apportioned   immunity   majority party
term limit   expulsion   floor leader
franking privilege   censure   president *pro tempore*

1. Serious misconduct by a member of Congress may end in that person's

_____ from office.

2. Members of Congress have the _____, or right to mail official letters or packages free of charge.

3. Members of Congress have _____, or legal protection.

4. The _____ for a member of the House is two years.

Chapter 5, Chapter Test Form C, continued

5. Formal disapproval of the actions of a member of Congress is called

_____ .

6. The party that has the most members in each house of Congress is called the

_____ .

7. A(n) _____ guides a particular party's proposed laws through Congress.

8. Congress determines how the seats in the House are to be

_____ every 10 years after the census is taken.

TRUE/FALSE *(2 points each)* Mark each statement *T* if it is true or *F* if it is false.

_____ **1.** Both the House of Representatives and the Senate make laws.

_____ **2.** If a representative cannot serve the entire term, the government must function with this vacancy.

_____ **3.** Many members of Congress have had little if any experience in politics before being elected.

_____ **4.** If serious problems arise after Congress has adjourned its regular session, the president may call Congress to meet in a special session.

_____ **5.** Each member of the House usually serves on three to five major standing committees.

_____ **6.** Usually a committee chairperson is the majority party member with the most years of service on the committee.

_____ **7.** Only in special circumstances can a person go to prison without a trial.

_____ **8.** Congress can raise and collect taxes, borrow money, and print and coin money.

_____ **9.** The powers of Congress are not limited.

_____ **10.** Both the Senate and the House of Representatives can revise a bill.

_____ **11.** The process by which a bill becomes a law is extremely short.

IDENTIFICATION *(3 points each)* Place the letter of the correct description into its proper place in the diagram.

a. Members serve two-year terms.

b. Members serve six-year terms.

c. can revise the content of a bill

d. has a majority and minority party

e. holds trials on impeachment charges

f. Members act as a jury in impeachment trial.

g. A bill is first introduced here.

h. The number of members is based on the size of state population.

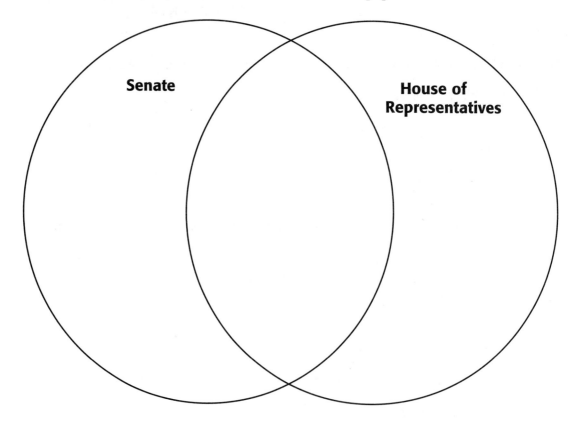

Name _____ Class _____ Date _____

Chapter Test Form C

The Executive Branch

MATCHING *(3 points each)* Place the letters of the descriptions next to the appropriate terms.

_____ **1.** presidential succession

_____ **2.** foreign policy

_____ **3.** treaties

_____ **4.** diplomacy

_____ **5.** diplomatic notes

_____ **6.** reprieve

_____ **7.** attorney general

_____ **8.** embassy

_____ **9.** civilian

_____ **10.** consulate

a. the art of interacting with foreign governments

b. the official residence of an ambassador in a foreign country

c. written agreements

d. the order in which the office of president is to be filled

e. written communications between the president and leaders of foreign nations

f. a nonmilitary person

g. the government's plan for interacting with other countries

h. the head of the Department of Justice

i. the office of a person who represents U.S. commercial interests in foreign countries

j. postpones the carrying out of a person's sentence

FILL IN THE BLANK *(3 points each)* Choose from the following list to complete each of the statements below.

pardon   consul
budget   executive departments
ministers   counterfeiting

1. The president may grant a(n) _____, freeing a person convicted of a crime from serving out the sentence.

2. A(n) _____ represents U.S. commercial interests in foreign countries.

3. A(n) _____ is a plan of income and spending.

4. As of 2003, there were 15 _____ in the federal government, each with specific areas of responsibility.

5. The Secret Service helps to prevent _____, or the making and distributing of fake money.

6. In a few smaller countries, _____ are ranked below ambassadors and represent the United States.

Chapter 6, Chapter Test Form C, continued

TRUE/FALSE *(2 points each)* Mark each statement *T* if it is true or *F* if it is false.

_____ **1.** To be elected president, one does not necessarily need to be a native-born U.S. citizen.

_____ **2.** John Adams said that the office of vice president was "the most significant" office ever invented.

_____ **3.** The vice president serves a four-year term.

_____ **4.** To be president, one must be at least 25 years of age.

_____ **5.** In recent years, presidents have given vice presidents more responsibilities.

_____ **6.** The president allows Congress to deal completely with economic concerns.

_____ **7.** The president serves as commander in chief of the armed forces.

_____ **8.** The president does not usually deal with foreign countries.

_____ **9.** The National Security Council is the president's top-ranking group of advisers on all matters concerning defense and security.

_____ **10.** The cabinet consists of the heads of the 15 executive departments and any other officials the president chooses.

_____ **11.** The Department of Agriculture helps farmers raise and market crops.

Chapter 6, Chapter Test Form C, continued

IDENTIFICATION (*3 points each*) Place the letter of the correct term into its proper place below to show what agencies help the president. The third level of boxes should indicate examples of those agencies.

a. cabinet

b. commander in chief

c. secretary of state

d. legislative leader

e. National Aeronautics and Space Administration

f. chief diplomat

g. foreign policy leader

h. independent agencies

i. Consumer Product Safety Commission

j. secretary of commerce

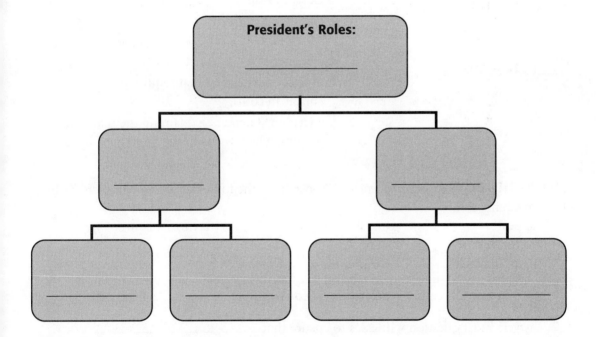

CHAPTER  7

Chapter Test Form C

The Judicial Branch

MATCHING *(3 points each)* Place the letters of the descriptions next to the appropriate terms.

_____ **1.** precedent

_____ **2.** constitutional law

_____ **3.** testimony

_____ **4.** original jurisdiction

_____ **5.** appellate jurisdiction

_____ **6.** subpoena

_____ **7.** magistrate judges

_____ **8.** circuit

_____ **9.** judicial review

_____ **10.** brief

a. having the authority to review decisions made by lower courts

b. officials that hear the evidence against an accused person and decide whether the case should be brought before a grand jury

c. law based on the Constitution and on Supreme Court decisions interpreting the Constitution

d. a large judicial district

e. earlier decision

f. the power to determine whether a law or a presidential action is in accord with the Constitution

g. having the authority to be the first courts in which most federal cases are heard

h. evidence given in court

i. official court orders that require people to appear in court

j. a written statement explaining the main points presented by lawyers to the Supreme Court

FILL IN THE BLANK *(3 points each)* Choose from the following list to complete each of the statements below.

appeal	marshal	territorial courts
testimony	hung jury	
court-martial	common	

1. If a jury cannot reach a verdict, it is called a(n) _____.

2. Lawyers must question witnesses to ensure that _____, or evidence given in court, is accurate.

3. To ensure that cases are decided fairly, the U.S. court system provides the right to a(n) _____, or request for review of the case.

4. Customary, or _____, law comes from judges' decisions.

5. One job of a(n) _____ is to deliver official court orders.

Chapter 7, Chapter Test Form C, continued

6. _____ were established by Congress to administer justice to people living in U.S. territorial possessions.

7. People in the armed services who are accused of breaking a military law are tried at a(n) _____ conducted by military officers.

TRUE/FALSE *(2 points each)* Mark each statement *T* if it is true or *F* if it is false.

_____ **1.** The Supreme Court reviews all cases that it receives on appeal.

_____ **2.** The Constitution requires that a Supreme Court justice be a lawyer.

_____ **3.** There are no limits on the Supreme Court's power.

_____ **4.** Justices are appointed to the Supreme Court for 10-year terms.

_____ **5.** U.S. law assumes that a person is guilty until proven innocent.

_____ **6.** An accused person may have a lawyer only if he or she can afford it.

_____ **7.** If a person is arrested on suspicion of a crime, he or she will certainly go to trial.

_____ **8.** Despite how serious a crime is, any accused person must be given a fair public trial.

_____ **9.** If the jury cannot reach a verdict, then the accused person is automatically set free.

_____ **10.** Appellate jurisdiction has authority over original jurisdiction.

_____ **11.** All federal courts are presided over by judges approved by the president and the Senate.

_____ **12.** The Sixth Amendment to the Constitution guarantees an accused person the right to be tried before a trial jury.

_____ **13.** It is possible that a person could appeal to the Supreme Court.

_____ **14.** Every American has the right to a fair public trial.

IDENTIFICATION *(3 points each)* First place the appropriate letters in the sections of the triangle to indicate the hierarchy of courts. Then insert to the right of each court the letters that show their characteristics.

   a. review cases that are appealed from the district courts
   b. where marshals and magistrate judges work
   c. Supreme Court
   d. district courts
   e. courts of appeals
   f. at least one in each of the 50 states and Washington, D.C.
   g. Decisions cannot be appealed and they are final.

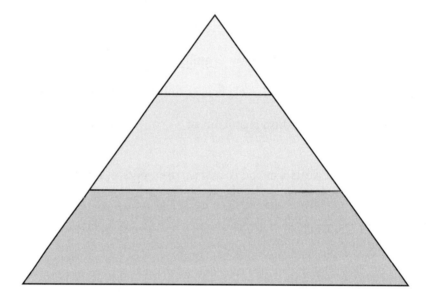

Name _____ Class _____ Date _____

Unit Test Form C

The Federal Government

MATCHING *(3 points each)* Place the letters of the descriptions next to the appropriate terms.

_____ **1.** Speaker

_____ **2.** constitutional law

_____ **3.** party whip

_____ **4.** elastic clause

_____ **5.** diplomatic notes

_____ **6.** constituents

_____ **7.** attorney general

_____ **8.** embassy

_____ **9.** brief

_____ **10.** original jurisdiction

a. states that Congress has the power "to make all laws which shall be necessary and proper for carrying into execution the foregoing powers"

b. the people who live in a congressmember's home district or state

c. the presiding officer of the House of Representatives

d. the official residence of an ambassador in a foreign country

e. written communications between the president and leaders of foreign nations

f. a written statement explaining the main points presented by lawyers to the Supreme Court

g. assists floor leaders in trying to persuade members to vote for party-sponsored legislation

h. the head of the Department of Justice

i. having the authority to be the first courts in which most federal cases are heard

j. law based on the Constitution and on Supreme Court decisions interpreting the Constitution

FILL IN THE BLANK *(3 points each)* Choose from the following list to complete each of the statements below.

franking privilege	consul	appeal
immunity	executive departments	apportioned
ministers	hung jury	term limit

1. Members of Congress have the _____, or right to mail official letters or packages free of charge.

2. To ensure that cases are decided fairly, the U.S. court system provides the right to

_____, or ask for a review of a case.

3. Members of Congress have _____, or legal protection.

4. The _____ for a member of the House is two years.

5. Congress determines how the seats in the House are to be

_____ every 10 years after the census is taken.

6. A(n) _____ represents U.S. commercial interests in foreign countries.

7. In a few smaller countries, _____ are ranked below ambassadors and represent the United States.

8. As of 2001, there were 14 _____ in the federal government, each with specific areas of responsibility.

9. If a jury cannot reach a verdict, it is called a(n) _____.

TRUE/FALSE *(2 points each)* Mark each statement *T* if it is true or *F* if it is false.

_____ **1.** The vice president serves a four-year term.

_____ **2.** If serious problems arise after Congress has adjourned its regular session, the president may call Congress to meet in a special session.

_____ **3.** An accused person may have a lawyer only if he or she can afford it.

_____ **4.** Usually a committee chairperson is the majority party member with the most years of service on the committee.

_____ **5.** The president serves as commander in chief of the armed forces.

_____ **6.** Appellate jurisdiction has authority over original jurisdiction.

_____ **7.** Both the Senate and the House of Representatives can revise a bill.

_____ **8.** To be elected president, one does not necessarily need to be a native-born U.S. citizen.

_____ **9.** Justices are appointed to the Supreme Court for 10-year terms.

_____ **10.** The Department of Agriculture helps farmers raise and market crops.

_____ **11.** The Supreme Court reviews all appeals cases that are submited.

Unit 2, Test Form C, continued

IDENTIFICATION *(3 points each)* First place the appropriate letters in the sections of the triangle to indicate the levels within the judicial branch. Then insert the letters of the job titles that serve within each level.

a. justices

b. Supreme Court

c. district courts

d. marshals

e. U.S. courts of appeals

f. magistrate judges

g. panel of judges

Judicial Branch

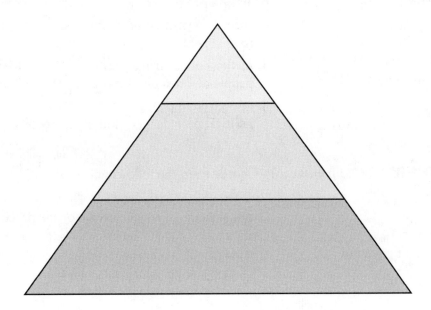

CHAPTER **8**   Chapter Test Form C

State Government

MATCHING *(3 points each)* Place the letters of the descriptions next to the appropriate terms.

_____ **1.** full faith and credit clause

_____ **2.** extradition

_____ **3.** proposition

_____ **4.** referendum

_____ **5.** executive orders

_____ **6.** warrant

_____ **7.** patronage

_____ **8.** penal code

_____ **9.** plaintiff

_____ **10.** small claims court

a. the orders that set up methods of enforcing laws

b. a set of criminal laws

c. ensures that each state will accept the court decisions and official records of other states

d. a proposed law

e. in a civil case, the person or company filing the lawsuit

f. returning fugitives to the state in which they committed the crime

g. an order to pay out money

h. special courts that hear civil cases involving less than $5,000

i. method of referring questions directly to the people before a bill is passed by the legislature

j. jobs given to people recommended by political party leaders and office holders

FILL IN THE BLANK *(3 points each)* Choose from the following list to complete each of the statements below.

territories   criminal cases   justice of the peace
governor   civil cases
lieutenant governor   complaint

1. A state's executive branch is headed by the _____.

2. _____ involve people who violate the law by harming individuals or the community.

3. The _____ of a state becomes head of the state executive branch if the governor dies, resigns, or is removed from office.

4. _____ deal with disputes between individuals or businesses.

5. Puerto Rico, Guam, American Samoa, and the U.S. Virgin Islands are examples

of U.S. _____.

6. A _____ is another word for a lawsuit.

7. A _____ hears minor cases in rural areas and small towns.

Chapter 8, Chapter Test Form C, continued

TRUE/FALSE *(2 points each)* Mark each statement *T* if it is true or *F* if it is false.

_____ **1.** The voters of each state elect officials such as lieutenant governor and secretary of state.

_____ **2.** The superintendent of public instruction is in charge of handling all state funds.

_____ **3.** All governors serve four-year terms.

_____ **4.** State legislatures may vote to pass a bill, change it, or kill it.

_____ **5.** Almost all states require that members of a state legislature live in the district they represent.

_____ **6.** All states have a bicameral legislature.

_____ **7.** A bill may be sent to a joint-conference committee so that both houses can reach a compromise.

_____ **8.** States rarely cooperate on projects that affect them both.

_____ **9.** Only the federal government can regulate trade between the states.

_____**10.** The Articles of Confederation allowed each state to issue its own money.

_____**11.** Hawaii was the last state to join the union.

Chapter 8, Chapter Test Form C, continued

IDENTIFICATION *(3 points each)* Place the letter of the correct word or phrase into its proper place in the diagram below.

a. lower
b. attorney general
c. House of Representatives
d. appeals
e. lieutenant governor

f. state supreme court
g. secretary of state
h. general trial
i. Senate

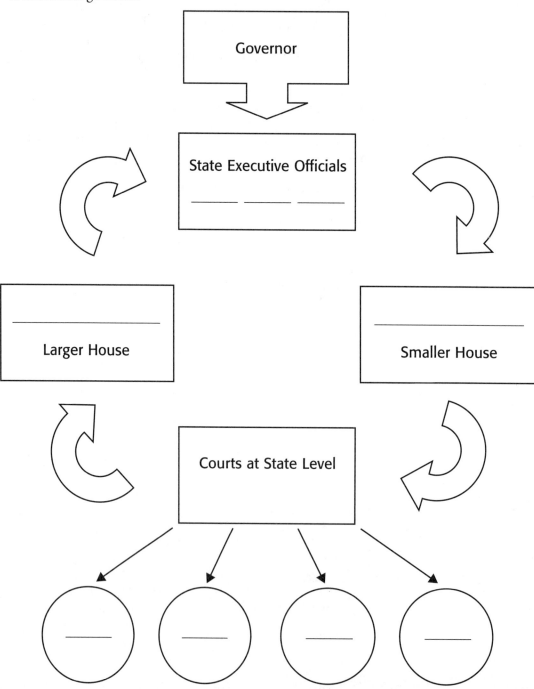

Name _____ Class _____ Date _____

Chapter Test Form C

Local Government

MATCHING *(3 points each)* Place the letters of the descriptions next to the appropriate terms.

_____ **1.** charter

_____ **2.** municipalities

_____ **3.** counties

_____ **4.** town meetings

_____ **5.** constables

_____ **6.** home rule

_____ **7.** mayor

_____ **8.** council member at large

_____ **9.** grant-in-aid

_____ **10.** block grant

a. enforce laws in township governments

b. a basic plan for a local governmental unit that defines its powers, responsibilities, and organization

c. funds given by the federal government for broadly defined purposes

d. States are divided into these units.

e. federal funds given to state and local governments for specific projects

f. A city has the power to write and amend its own municipal charter.

g. a council member who is chosen by all the voters in a city

h. units of local government that are incorporated by the state and include cities, villages, and boroughs

i. chief executive of city government who sees that ordinances are enforced

j. when town residents gather to discuss business in the town hall

FILL IN THE BLANK *(3 points each)* Choose from the following list to complete each of the statements below.

ordinance	commission	city council
county clerk	district attorney	sheriff
wards	county seat	special district

1. A(n) _____ is a regulation that governs the community.

2. _____ is the lawmaking body of the mayor-council government.

3. Under the mayor-council form of government, a city is divided into several districts, or _____.

4. A city may be governed by a _____ in which three to nine elected officials act as the lawmaking and executive body.

5. The role of a(n) _____ is to keep records of births, deaths, election results, and marriages.

6. A charter may set up a(n) _____ to address a certain need, such as irrigation.

7. A(n) _____ represents the state government in county trials.

8. A(n) _____ enforces the law and chooses deputies to assist with law enforcement.

9. Plantation owners in each county met regularly in a centrally located town known as

the _____.

TRUE/FALSE *(2 points each)* Mark each statement *T* if it is true or *F* if it is false.

_____ **1.** Building roads is a cooperative effort among local, state, and federal governments.

_____ **2.** Fire alarms that go off in a certain neighborhood may only be answered by the neighborhood's fire department.

_____ **3.** Federal, state, and local governments sometimes compete with one another.

_____ **4.** State governments grant funds to communities to help them operate schools.

_____ **5.** Actual control of schools is left to the federal government.

_____ **6.** A city government may take one of three forms: a mayor-council government, a commission government, or a council-manager government.

_____ **7.** Under a strong-mayor plan, mayors can hire and dismiss city officials.

_____ **8.** City governments do not necessarily need to receive charters from state legislatures.

_____ **9.** The mayor is appointed by the city council.

_____ **10.** During town meetings in early New England towns, representatives chosen by citizens decided what was best for the town.

_____ **11.** Early towns and villages differed only in population.

_____ **12.** Every state has 200 counties.

_____ **13.** The county form of government was formed within the past 100 years.

_____ **14.** The group of officials at the head of a county government is elected by Congress.

Chapter 9, Chapter Test Form C, continued

IDENTIFICATION *(3 points each)* Place the letter of the correct description into its proper place in the diagram below.

    a. Here residents attended meetings and voiced their opinions concerning certain issues.

    b. Made up of only homes and other buildings, not outlying parts of the settlement

    c. Has a large population in a relatively small area

    d. States are divided into these areas. Number and sizes vary from state to state.

    e. These eventually developed into county-township government or congressional townships.

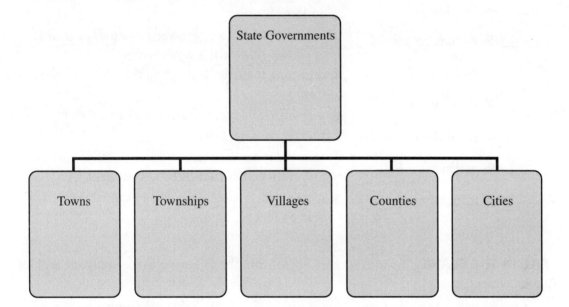

UNIT **3**

Unit Test Form C

State and Local Government

MATCHING *(3 points each)* Place the letters of the descriptions next to the appropriate terms.

_____ **1.** extradition

_____ **2.** coalition

_____ **3.** warrant

_____ **4.** penal code

_____ **5.** electoral votes

_____ **6.** plaintiff

_____ **7.** closed primary

_____ **8.** small claims court

_____ **9.** precincts

_____ **10.** referendum

a. the person or company filing a lawsuit in a civil case

b. method of referring questions directly to voters before a bill is passed by the legislature

c. an order to pay out money

d. voting districts made by dividing counties, cities, and wards

e. only voters who are registered in a party can vote to choose that party's candidates

f. returning fugitives to the state that they ran away from

g. votes made by members of the electoral college

h. a set of criminal laws

i. agreement between two or more political parties to work together to run the government

j. special courts that hear civil cases involving less than $5,000

FILL IN THE BLANK *(3 points each)* Choose from the following list to complete each of the statements below.

territories
lieutenant governor
civil cases

criminal cases
presidential primaries
popular vote

nominate
straight ticket

1. The _____ of a state becomes head of the state executive branch if the governor dies, resigns, or is removed from office.

2. Puerto Rico, Guam, American Samoa, and the U.S. Virgin Islands are examples of

U.S. _____.

3. If you were to vote for all Democrats, you would be voting a

_____.

4. In _____, voters indicate which candidate they want the delegates to vote for at the national nominating convention.

5. _____ deal with disputes between individuals or businesses.

Unit 3, Test Form C, continued

6. The _____ refers to the votes cast by citizens.

7. _____ involve people who violate the law by harming individuals or the community.

8. Political parties _____, or select, men or women to run for public office.

TRUE/FALSE *(2 points each)* Mark each statement *T* if it is true or *F* if it is false.

_____ **1.** The Articles of Confederation allowed each state to issue its own money.

_____ **2.** Each state has the right to refuse to accept the decisions of courts in other states.

_____ **3.** Governments that have a one-party system are usually dictatorships or totalitarian governments.

_____ **4.** Precinct captains distribute information about a campaign and get to know people in the neighborhood.

_____ **5.** Most states require voters to register before the day of an election.

_____ **6.** One example of a concurrent power is the power of taxation.

_____ **7.** Only if both houses pass a bill in the same form can it be sent to the governor to be signed.

_____ **8.** A state's department of public works is responsible for all public construction projects in the state, including work done on interstate highways.

_____ **9.** During the election campaign, candidates usually stay close to home and work on strategies.

_____**10.** In many states, the law provides that all employers must give time off during the day to any employee who wants to vote.

_____**11.** U.S. citizens of any age can vote.

Unit 3, Test Form C, continued

IDENTIFICATION *(3 points each)* Place the letters of the correct terms in the spaces below.

a. lieutenant governor

b. president

c. governor

d. vice president

e. electoral votes

f. popular vote

	State Level	National Level
Title of leader		
How elected		
Title of person who would take over if leader is unable to serve		

CHAPTER **10**

Chapter Test Form C
Electing Leaders

MATCHING *(3 points each)* Place the letters of the descriptions next to the appropriate terms.

_____ **1.** candidates

_____ **2.** coalition

_____ **3.** one-party system

_____ **4.** precincts

_____ **5.** independent voters

_____ **6.** closed primary

_____ **7.** grassroots

_____ **8.** secret ballot

_____ **9.** party platform

_____ **10.** electoral votes

a. a system of government in which there is only one political party

b. a way of voting that keeps a vote confidential

c. voters who are not members of a political party

d. agreement between two or more political parties to work together to run the government

e. votes made by members of the electoral college

f. only voters who are registered in a party can vote to choose that party's candidates

g. support from many individuals at the local level rather than from national parties

h. men and women who run for election to offices at various levels of government

i. a written statement that outlines a party's views on important issues

j. voting districts made by dividing counties, cities, and wards

FILL IN THE BLANK *(3 points each)* Choose from the following list to complete each of the statements below.

multiparty system   straight ticket   popular vote
nominate   primary election   presidential primaries
third-party   favorite sons or daughters

1. The _____ refers to the votes cast by all citizens.

2. Political parties _____, or select, men or women to run for public office.

3. Theodore Roosevelt and Ross Perot ran for office as _____ candidates.

4. In _____, voters indicate which candidate they want the delegates to vote for at the national nominating convention.

5. If you were to vote for all Democrats, you would be voting a

_____.

6. Party leaders who are popular in their home states are called _____.

7. Many European countries have a _____, in which there are more than two strong political parties.

8. The _____ allows voters to choose candidates from each party who will run in the later general election.

TRUE/FALSE *(2 points each)* Mark each statement *T* if it is true or *F* if it is false.

_____ **1.** A woman has never been nominated for the vice presidency.

_____ **2.** In the presidential election, Americans do not vote directly for the president.

_____ **3.** Electors are not required to vote for their party's candidate.

_____ **4.** Those people who have registered as independent voters cannot vote in a closed primary.

_____ **5.** In general, independent candidates are elected more often than major-party candidates.

_____ **6.** It is rare that a person would be elected to office by write-in votes.

_____ **7.** A person must register as a member of a political party.

_____ **8.** A U.S. citizen of any age can vote.

_____ **9.** Precincts make voting easier for citizens and more efficient for election officials.

_____ **10.** Candidates running for election may raise as much money as they can from any source they want.

_____ **11.** Once a person joins a political party, he or she cannot leave that party.

_____ **12.** Thomas Jefferson led what was then called the Democratic-Republican Party.

_____ **13.** President George Washington believed that political parties were dangerous and could divide the country.

_____ **14.** Governments that have a one-party system are usually dictatorships or totalitarian governments.

IDENTIFICATION *(3 points each)* Place the letter of the correct word or phrase into its proper place in the diagram below.

a. register

b. receive the majority of the electoral votes

c. be at least 18 years old

d. have grassroots support

e. be a registered Democrat

f. be elected by state convention

Qualifications

In order to vote in the United States, you must...	
In order to vote for a Democrat in a closed primary, you must...	
In order to win the presidency, a candidate must...	
In order to run as an independent candidate, you must ...	
In order to be elected to the national committee, you must...	

Name _____ Class _____ Date _____

MATCHING *(3 points each)* Place the letters of the descriptions next to the appropriate terms.

_____ **1.** interest groups

_____ **2.** lobby

_____ **3.** volunteers

_____ **4.** propaganda

_____ **5.** political action committees

_____ **6.** lobbyist

_____ **7.** public opinion

_____ **8.** public interest groups

_____ **9.** poll

_____ **10.** mass media

a. the total of opinions held concerning a particular issue

b. collect voluntary contributions from members and use this money to fund candidates that the committees favor

c. people who work without pay to help others

d. groups that seek to promote the interests of the general public rather than just one part of it

e. organizations of people with a common interest that try to influence government policies and decisions

f. a survey

g. a pressure group

h. a person who is paid by an interest group to represent that group's interests

i. spreading ideas to influence people

j. various forms of communication that transmit information to large numbers of people

FILL IN THE BLANK *(3 points each)* Choose from the following list to complete each of the statements below.

public opinion	revealed propaganda	name-calling
mass media	testimonials	plain-folks appeal
concealed propaganda	bandwagon	poll

1. _____ makes readers or listeners aware that someone is trying to influence them.

2. People who write _____ forms of propaganda believe that if you say something often enough and loud enough, many people will believe it.

3. _____ is information that is presented as being factual while its sources are kept secret.

4. _____ is the use of an unpleasant label or description to harm a person, group, or product.

5. _____ is defined as the total of the opinions held concerning a particular issue.

Chapter 11, Chapter Test Form C, continued

6. _____ is a propaganda technique in which political candidates and advertisers seek endorsements from famous people.

7. Forms of _____ include newspapers, television, radio, films, books, and magazines.

8. When a candidate describes himself or herself as a plain, hardworking citizen, he or she is using a _____.

9. Using a _____, or survey, is one way to measure public opinion.

TRUE/FALSE *(2 points each)* Mark each statement *T* if it is true or *F* if it is false.

_____ **1.** Lobbyists are not required to reveal to the government who they work for and how much money they spend in lobbying.

_____ **2.** Public interest groups seek to promote one part of the general public's interests.

_____ **3.** Lobbyists were once viewed with a great deal of suspicion.

_____ **4.** One example of an issue many interest groups struggle over is the minimum wage law.

_____ **5.** Interest groups differ in size and budgets but not goals.

_____ **6.** Citizen involvement hinders democracy.

_____ **7.** Almost every American citizen votes in elections.

_____ **8.** The number of political action committees has decreased in recent years.

_____ **9.** Government officials in the United States are selected by a small percentage of the country's people.

_____ **10.** Interest groups may provide volunteers to help candidates who are sympathetic to their causes.

_____ **11.** Growth of the mass media and advances in technology have decreased the amount of propaganda.

_____ **12.** Sometimes people may respond a certain way to a poll so that they appear to support a winner.

_____ **13.** Public opinion refers to one opinion.

_____ **14.** Most lobbyists work independently and have little or no staff.

IDENTIFICATION *(3 points each)* We are influenced by many factors when it comes time to vote. Place the letter of the correct term into its proper place in the diagram below.

a. distribute literature

b. mass media

c. glittering generalities

d. community action

e. National Organization for Women

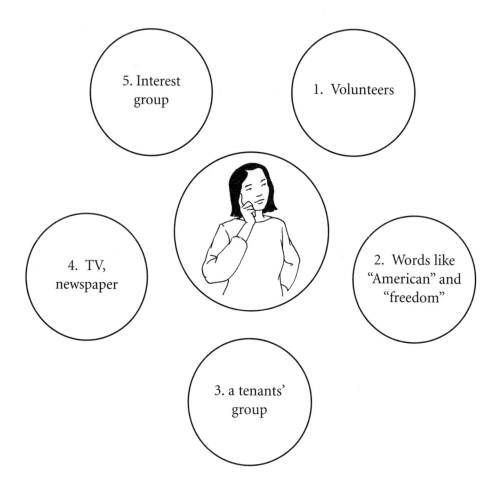

5. Interest group

1. Volunteers

4. TV, newspaper

2. Words like "American" and "freedom"

3. a tenants' group

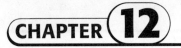

CHAPTER **12**   Chapter Test Form C

Paying for Government

MATCHING *(3 points each)* Place the letters of the descriptions next to the appropriate terms.

_____ **1.** national debt

_____ **2.** revenue

_____ **3.** income taxes

_____ **4.** progressive tax

_____ **5.** sales tax

_____ **6.** regressive tax

_____ **7.** tariff

_____ **8.** balanced budget

_____ **9.** deficit

_____ **10.** audit

a. tax collected on most products sold

b. a tax that takes a larger percentage of income from lower-income groups than from higher-income groups

c. taxes on the earnings of individuals and companies

d. a shortage of money

e. a tax that takes a larger percentage of income from higher-income groups than from lower-income groups

f. money

g. a careful examination by trained accountants of every item of income and expenditure

h. when revenue equals expenditures

i. the total amount of money that the government has borrowed, plus interest

j. an import tax

FILL IN THE BLANK *(3 points each)* Choose from the following list to complete each of the statements below.

interest	bond	profit
fees	exemption	real property
fines	deductions	personal property

1. _____ is the payment made for the use of borrowed money.

2. Land, buildings, and other structures are examples of _____.

3. Small payments called _____ are charged for types of licenses.

4. Illegal parking, speeding, and other traffic violations may result in

_____.

5. Stocks, bonds, jewelry, cars, and boats are examples of _____.

6. A government _____ is a certificate stating that the government has borrowed a certain sum of money from its owner.

7. Taxpayers can claim charitable contributions and most business expenses as

_____ .

8. _____ is the income a business has left after paying its expenses.

9. A(n) _____ is an amount of money a taxpayer may subtract from his or her tax payment for himself or herself and for each dependent.

TRUE/FALSE *(2 points each)* Mark each statement *T* if it is true or *F* if it is false.

_____ **1.** All citizens pay the same amount of taxes, regardless of income.

_____ **2.** The government does not have to pay interest on the money it borrows.

_____ **3.** During the 1990s, the government spent less money on defense.

_____ **4.** The largest source of revenue for the federal government is income taxes.

_____ **5.** State and city governments do not collect individual income taxes.

_____ **6.** The amount taxed for personal property is usually very high.

_____ **7.** Much of the funding for public schools in the United States comes from local property taxes.

_____ **8.** Government officials must decide which activities need funding more quickly because there is not enough money to fund all of them.

_____ **9.** Citizens and businesses are not required to pay taxes.

_____**10.** Governments borrow money by issuing bonds.

_____**11.** Taxes are taken out of one's income only once a year.

_____**12.** Social Security tax paid by each worker is matched by the employer.

_____**13.** Excise taxes are collected on items such as gasoline and luxury automobiles.

_____**14.** The amount of income tax that people pay may change from year to year.

Chapter 12, Test Form C, *continued*

IDENTIFICATION *(3 points each)* There are several different types of taxes that must be paid to the government. Match the letter of each tax listed below to its associated illustration.

a. excise tax

b. income tax

c. Social Security tax

d. gift tax

e. sales tax

UNIT **4**

Unit Test Form C

The Citizen in Government

MATCHING *(3 points each)* Place the letters of the descriptions next to the appropriate terms.

_____ **1.** counties

_____ **2.** balanced budget

_____ **3.** political action committees

_____ **4.** audit

_____ **5.** block grant

_____ **6.** public interest groups

_____ **7.** deficit

_____ **8.** municipalities

_____ **9.** tariff

_____ **10.** mass media

a. groups that seek to promote the interests of the general public rather than just one part of it

b. a careful examination by trained accountants of every item of income and expenditure

c. collect voluntary contributions from members and use this money to fund candidates that the committees favor

d. funds given by the federal government for broadly defined purposes

e. a shortage of money

f. states are divided into these units

g. various forms of communication that transmit information to large numbers of people

h. when revenue equals expenditures

i. units of local government that are incorporated by the state and include cities, villages, and boroughs

j. an import tax

FILL IN THE BLANK *(3 points each)* Choose from the following list to complete each of the statements below.

county clerk   public opinion   special district
city council   personal property   bond
revealed propaganda   interest

1. Stocks, bonds, jewelry, cars, and boats are examples of _____.

2. _____ is the payment made for the use of borrowed money.

3. _____ is the lawmaking body of the mayor-council government.

4. A charter may set up a(n) _____ to address a certain need, such as irrigation.

5. A government _____ is a certificate stating that the government has borrowed a certain sum of money from its owner.

Unit 4, Test Form C, continued

6. _____ makes readers or listeners aware that someone is trying to influence them.

7. The role of a(n) _____ is to keep records of births, deaths, election results, and marriages.

8. _____ is defined as the total of the opinions held concerning a particular issue.

TRUE/FALSE *(2 points each)* Mark each statement *T* if it is true or *F* if it is false.

_____ **1.** Actual control of schools is left to the federal government.

_____ **2.** City governments do not necessarily need to receive charters from state legislatures.

_____ **3.** Federal, state, and local governments compete with one another.

_____ **4.** The county form of government was formed within the past 100 years.

_____ **5.** Lobbyists are not required to reveal to the government who they work for and how much money they spend in lobbying.

_____ **6.** The minimum wage law is one example of an issue many interest groups struggle with.

_____ **7.** Government officials in the United States are selected by a small percentage of the country's people.

_____ **8.** All citizens pay the same amount of taxes, regardless of income.

_____ **9.** Much of the funding for public schools in the United States comes from local property taxes.

_____ **10.** Taxes are taken out of one's income only once a year.

_____ **11.** Excise taxes are collected on things like gasoline and luxury automobiles.

Unit 4, Test Form C, continued

IDENTIFICATION *(3 points each)* Place the letter of the correct word or phrase in the spaces below.

a. gift tax

b. collected on "luxury" services and goods

c. collected from all the wealth a person leaves his or her heirs

d. collected on most products sold

e. Social Security tax

f. collected on portion of estate inherited by an individual

g. property tax

h. collected on earnings of individuals and companies

Type of Tax	What is Taxed
Sales tax	**1.**
Excise tax	**2.**
3.	Value of property owned by a person or business
Inheritance tax	**4.**
5.	A gift worth more than $10,000
Income tax	**6.**
Estate tax	**7.**
8.	Part of a worker's income that is paid to retired people and people with disabilities

Name _____ Class _____ Date _____

Chapter Test Form C

Citizenship and the Family

MATCHING *(3 points each)* In the space provided, write the letter of the description that matches each term.

_____ **1.** family law

_____ **2.** child abuse

_____ **3.** foster homes

_____ **4.** guardian

_____ **5.** adopt

_____ **6.** divorce

_____ **7.** fixed expenses

_____ **8.** no-fault divorce

_____ **9.** remarriage

_____ **10.** blended family

a. the final legal ending of a marriage

b. a person appointed by a state court to care for an individual who is not an adult or who is unable to care for him- or herself

c. a system under which people seeking divorce do not have to charge their partners with specific reasons or grounds for a divorce

d. expenses that occur regularly and must be paid

e. emotional abuse, physical injury, or sexual abuse inflicted on a child

f. stepfamilies

g. to legally establish a child as one's own

h. regulates marriage, divorce, and the responsibilities and rights of adults and children in the family

i. a marriage in which one partner has been married before

j. homes of people who are unrelated to the children but who agree to act as their caregivers

FILL IN THE BLANK *(3 points each)* Choose the correct items from the following list to complete the statements below.

delayed marriage   compromises
two-income family   blended families
single-parent families

1. Conflicts that occur between family members require them to make

_____—to give a little and take a little.

2. A family in which both partners work is referred to as a _____.

3. More than 27 percent of American families with children under the age of 18 are

_____.

4. _____ occur when one or both partners bring children from previous relationships into a new marriage.

5. Marrying at an older age is called a _____.

Chapter 13, Chapter Test Form C, continued

TRUE/FALSE *(2 points each)* Mark each statement *T* if it is true or *F* if it is false.

_____ **1.** If family members do not work together to find solutions to problems, the problems may develop into crises.

_____ **2.** A child's earliest ideas of right and wrong are taught in the home.

_____ **3.** Budgets usually mean complicated bookkeeping and "pinching pennies."

_____ **4.** Social scientists say that one reason for the high divorce rate today is because the divorce process has become less complicated.

_____ **5.** Most states allow people of any age to marry.

_____ **6.** There are few laws protecting the rights of families.

_____ **7.** In the past few decades, the American family has undergone many changes.

_____ **8.** In colonial days, families produced most of what they needed to survive.

_____ **9.** When colonial children got married, they usually brought their spouses to live with them on the family farm.

_____ **10.** As people began moving to the city, families had to rely more on outside sources for food and education.

_____ **11.** Using self-restraint and considering other people's points of view help prevent serious conflict.

_____ **12.** Conflicts rarely occur between parents.

_____ **13.** Some parents give their children an allowance to teach them financial responsibilities.

_____ **14.** Hardly any children worked in factories in the 1800s.

Chapter 13, Chapter Test Form C, continued

IDENTIFICATION *(3 points each)* Place the letter of the correct terms in the spaces below.

a. delayed marriage
b. cost of food
c. emotional abuse
d. single-parent families
e. two-income families
f. physical injury
g. house payments
h. medical expenses

Trends in Families	Problems in Some Families	Family Expenses

Name _____ Class _____ Date _____

Citizenship in School

MATCHING *(3 points each)* In the space provided, write the letter of the description that matches each term.

_____ **1.** insight

_____ **2.** mainstreaming

_____ **3.** community colleges

_____ **4.** habit

_____ **5.** experience

_____ **6.** graduate school

_____ **7.** prejudice

_____ **8.** critical thinking

_____ **9.** motivation

_____ **10.** extracurricular activities

a. the direct observation of or participation in events

b. an action that is performed automatically without thinking

c. education beyond college or a university

d. examples of these include school clubs, sports teams, and drama

e. a type of reasoning that is made up of a number of steps

f. occurs after we have studied a problem and ruled out several possible answers

g. schools that are often supported by taxpayers and offer courses at low tuition to high school graduates

h. an opinion that is not based on a careful and reasonable investigation of the facts

i. the practice of including students with special needs in regular classrooms

j. the internal drive that directs people's behavior

FILL IN THE BLANK *(3 points each)* Choose the correct items from the following list to complete the statements below.

colleges   creativity   extracurricular activities
university   community colleges
conditioning   prejudice

1. The ability to find new ways of thinking and doing things is called

_____.

2. An example of a _____ is assuming all boys with brown hair are intelligent.

3. Learning in which an action is produced as a result of past experience is called

_____.

Chapter 14, Chapter Test Form C, continued

4. Junior colleges, or _____, offer two-year degrees.

5. A _____ contains one or more colleges.

6. Those things a student does at school outside of academic work are called

_____.

TRUE/FALSE *(2 points each)* Mark each statement *T* if it is true or *F* if it is false.

_____ **1.** The first major step in developing public education was taken in Rhode Island in 1647.

_____ **2.** Citizens are entitled to a free public education from kindergarten through high school.

_____ **3.** The three kinds of high schools are academic, technical, and vocational.

_____ **4.** The science, math, and reading test scores of American students are lower at most levels than those in other industrial countries.

_____ **5.** Schools aim to teach reading, writing, arithmetic, and citizenship.

_____ **6.** The success you enjoy in school and the study and learning habits you develop do not play a role in the kind of person you will become.

_____ **7.** Reviewing with other students before a test is helpful.

_____ **8.** In thinking through an issue, it is important to learn to weigh all the evidence.

_____ **9.** Few people can be impartial all of the time.

_____ **10.** Much of what we know is learned by looking and listening.

_____ **11.** Schools teach students how to best use information by analyzing and putting facts together and by drawing conclusions about the facts.

IDENTIFICATION *(3 points each)* Write the letter of the correct word or phrase in its proper place below. Place the schools in the order of the ages of the students who attend them.

  a. ages five and six
  b. middle school
  c. high school
  d. grades seven, eight, and nine
  e. kindergarten
  f. grades four through eight
  g. junior high
  h. elementary school
  i. grades nine through twelve
  j. grades one through five or eight

Types of Schools	Ages or Grades of Students

CHAPTER  **15**

Chapter Test Form C

Citizenship in the Community

MATCHING *(3 points each)* Place the letters of the descriptions next to the appropriate terms.

_____ **1.** crossroads

_____ **2.** metropolitan area

_____ **3.** megalopolis

_____ **4.** communication

_____ **5.** recreation

_____ **6.** compulsory

a. the passing along of information, ideas, and beliefs from one person to another

b. where two main roads meet

c. required by law

d. relaxation or amusement

e. a large city and its surrounding towns

f. a continuous urban chain

FILL IN THE BLANK *(3 points each)* Choose the correct items from the following list to complete the statements below.

metropolitan area	recreation	volunteer groups
megalopolis	compulsory	suburbs
communication	crossroads	

1. A _____ was generally a good place to sell supplies to local farmers and travelers.

2. _____ include towns or villages outside of a city.

3. It is _____ that children attend school.

4. Writing and speaking are forms of _____.

5. Chicago is an example of a _____.

6. Playing sports is an example of _____.

7. The American Red Cross and the Boy Scouts are examples of _____.

8. Areas such as Boston and New York City are examples of a _____.

Chapter 15, Chapter Test Form C, continued

TRUE/FALSE *(2 points each)* Mark each statement *T* if it is true or *F* if it is false.

_____ **1.** Most farms grow the same types of crops, regardless of their location.

_____ **2.** Most large inland cities were established on lake ports or along major rivers.

_____ **3.** A community's climate and resources do not affect the types of government services needed by the people living there.

_____ **4.** There are now two rural Americas.

_____ **5.** Many American communities grew because they were located on transportation routes.

_____ **6.** The railroad hindered cities' growth.

_____ **7.** Recreational facilities should allow people to do interesting and healthy activities.

_____ **8.** Local courts, judges, and law enforcement officers help maintain peace and order in a community.

_____ **9.** People may form communities to provide better services to citizens.

_____**10.** No citizenship services are compulsory.

_____**11.** Pittsburgh, Pennsylvania, once had a major problem with pollution.

_____**12.** Many cities have begun to rebuild older areas of the city.

_____**13.** Retired people are unable to volunteer.

_____**14.** One responsibility you have as a citizen is to pick up litter.

Chapter 15, Chapter Test Form C, *continued*

IDENTIFICATION *(3 points each)* Fill in the chart below, matching the type of community with its characteristics.

  a. metropolitan area
  b. small country town
  c. town located on outskirts of city
  d. rural farm community
  e. cities of 2,500 people or more
  f. suburb
  g. grow crops based on climate
  h. urban area
  i. population is less than 2,500
  j. cities and their surrounding towns and suburbs

Type of Community	Characteristics

Chapter Test Form C

Citizenship and the Law

MATCHING *(3 points each)* In the space provided, write the letter of the description that matches each term.

_____ **1.** criminal

_____ **2.** felonies

_____ **3.** misdemeanors

_____ **4.** homicide

_____ **5.** aggravated assault

_____ **6.** forcible rape

_____ **7.** petty larceny

_____ **8.** white-collar crimes

_____ **9.** robbery

_____ **10.** fraud

a. the sexual violation of a person by force and against the person's will

b. less serious offenses such as traffic violations and disorderly conduct

c. taking something from a person by threatening the person with injury

d. taking someone else's money or property through dishonesty

e. any kind of physical injury that is done intentionally to another person

f. crimes committed for illegal gain by people in the course of their work

g. a person who commits any type of crime

h. the theft of goods valued under a certain amount

i. serious crimes such as homicide and kidnapping

j. the killing of one person by another person

FILL IN THE BLANK *(3 points each)* Choose the correct items from the following list to complete the statements below.

criminal justice system   arraigned   acquitted
community policing   defense   plea bargain
probable cause   parole

1. The _____ represents the accused person's side of the case.

2. The three-part system of police, courts, and corrections used to bring criminals to

justice is known as the _____.

3. A police officer must have _____ to make an arrest; in other words, he or she must have witnessed a crime or gathered enough evidence to make an arrest.

4. In _____, officers are encouraged to get to know the people who live and work in the neighborhood.

5. In a(n) _____, an accused person pleads guilty to a lesser offense than the original charge.

6. When a person is _____, he or she enters a plea of guilty or not guilty to a charge.

7. Many prisoners may be eligible for _____, or early release.

8. If a person is _____ of a crime, he or she is found not guilty.

TRUE/FALSE *(2 points each)* Mark each statement *T* if it is true or *F* if it is false.

_____ **1.** Immediately after being arrested, a person goes to trial.

_____ **2.** The sole purpose of imprisonment is retribution, or revenge.

_____ **3.** One possible outcome for a juvenile offender is probation.

_____ **4.** Before the late 1800s, juveniles at least 7 years old were held responsible for their crimes.

_____ **5.** People can commit crimes against other people, but not property.

_____ **6.** The national crime bill passed in 1994 involves life sentences for three-time violent offenders.

_____ **7.** Crime rates have dropped in the past decade.

_____ **8.** The FBI identifies 300 types of crime.

_____ **9.** When people are arrested, they must be told by the police officer that they have the right to remain silent.

_____ **10.** All citizens support capital punishment.

_____ **11.** All states consider juveniles to be young people under the age of 18.

_____ **12.** Anyone is allowed to become involved in a juvenile court hearing.

_____ **13.** Poor home conditions and juvenile crime are not connected.

_____ **14.** Young people who drop out of school and are unemployed often are at greater risk of becoming involved in criminal activities.

IDENTIFICATION *(3 points each)* Fill in the chart below, matching the person with the appropriate description.

  a. adults who commit any type of crime

  b. usually under the age of 18

  c. must pass physical examinations in training

  d. may commit embezzlement to support their children

  e. experience hearings instead of trials

  f. main responsibility is to prevent crime

Police Officers	Criminals	Juvenile Delinquents

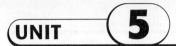

UNIT 5

Test Form C

The Citizen in Society

MATCHING *(3 points each)* In the space provided, write the letter of the description that matches each term.

_____ **1.** child abuse

_____ **2.** communication

_____ **3.** creativity

_____ **4.** homicide

_____ **5.** divorce

_____ **6.** petty larceny

_____ **7.** experience

_____ **8.** blended family

_____ **9.** compulsory

_____ **10.** robbery

a. the ability to find new ways of thinking and doing things

b. the killing of one person by another person

c. the passing along of information, ideas, and beliefs from one person to another

d. stepfamily

e. the theft of goods valued under a certain amount

f. taking something from a person by threatening the person with injury

g. emotional abuse, physical injury, or sexual abuse inflicted on a child by another person

h. the direct observation of or participation in events

i. required by law

j. the final legal ending of a marriage

FILL IN THE BLANK *(3 points each)* Choose from the following list to complete each of the statements below.

motivation	recreation	community colleges
two-income family	delayed marriage	community policing
crossroads	probable cause	

1. Playing sports is an example of _____.

2. A _____ was generally a good place to sell supplies to local farmers and travelers.

3. A family in which both partners work is referred to as a _____.

4. _____ is the internal drive that stirs people and directs their behavior and attitudes.

5. Marrying at an older age is also called a _____.

6. A police officer must have _____ to make an arrest; in other words, he or she must have witnessed a crime or gathered enough evidence to make an arrest.

7. Junior colleges, or _____, offer two-year degrees.

8. In _____, officers are encouraged to get to know the people who live and work in the neighborhood.

TRUE/FALSE *(2 points each)* Mark each statement *T* if it is true or *F* if it is false.

_____ **1.** Social scientists say that one reason for the high divorce rate today is that the divorce process has become less complicated.

_____ **2.** Citizens are entitled to a free public education from kindergarten through high school.

_____ **3.** Local courts, judges, and law enforcement officers help maintain peace and order in a community.

_____ **4.** People can commit crimes against other people, but not property.

_____ **5.** As people began moving to the city, families had to rely more on outside sources for food and education.

_____ **6.** The science, math, and reading test scores of American students are lower at most levels than those in other industrial countries.

_____ **7.** Pittsburgh, Pennsylvania, once had a major problem with pollution.

_____ **8.** All states consider juveniles to be young people under the age of 18.

_____ **9.** If family members do not work together to find solutions to problems, problems may develop into crises.

_____ **10.** *Kindergarten* in German means "garden for children."

_____ **11.** There are now two rural Americas.

_____ **12.** The sole purpose of imprisonment is retribution, or revenge.

_____ **13.** All citizens support capital punishment.

_____ **14.** There are few laws protecting the rights of families.

Unit 5, Test Form C, continued

IDENTIFICATION *(3 points each)* Place the letters of the correct terms or phrases in the spaces below.

   a. lack parental guidance

   b. poverty

   c. drug use

   d. involvement in gangs

   e. crime

   f. parents' use of illegal drugs

Problems in Some Families	Possible Effects

CHAPTER **17**

Chapter Test Form C

The Economic System

MATCHING *(3 points each)* Place the letters of the descriptions next to the appropriate terms.

_____ **1.** rent

_____ **2.** gross income

_____ **3.** free market

_____ **4.** labor

_____ **5.** patent

_____ **6.** productivity

_____ **7.** trust

_____ **8.** entrepreneur

_____ **9.** net income

_____ **10.** economies of scale

a. describes the situation in which goods can be produced more efficiently by larger companies

b. created when several companies create a board of trustees

c. all human effort used to produce goods and services

d. money left over after all costs have been paid

e. exchange between buyers and sellers who are free to choose how they operate

f. the amount of work produced by a worker in an hour

g. the money a person pays to use land or other property belonging to someone else

h. gives a person the exclusive right to make and sell an invention for a certain number of years

i. a business owner

j. the total amount of money a firm receives from the sale of its goods or services

FILL IN THE BLANK *(3 points each)* Choose the correct items from the following list to complete the statements below.

market economy	invest	monopoly
free competition	law of demand	stockholders
corporation	dividends	nonprofit organizations

1. The _____ states that buyers will demand more products when they can buy them at lower prices.

2. Corporation profits paid to people who hold stock are called

_____.

3. An economy in which people have the freedom to buy and sell what they choose when they choose is called a(n) _____.

4. _____ provide goods and services without seeking to earn a profit.

5. A(n) _____ is the most common form of business organization for the country's large companies.

6. People who buy corporate stocks are called _____.

7. A company is a(n) _____ if it is the only firm selling a product or producing a service.

8. To _____ in businesses and valuable goods is to put money into them.

9. In a system of _____, each business tries to persuade people to buy what it has to offer.

TRUE/FALSE *(2 points each)* Mark each statement *T* if it is true or *F* if it is false.

_____ **1.** Sole proprietorships usually have two to three owners.

_____ **2.** Each share of stock entitles its owner to two votes for the board of directors' election.

_____ **3.** The American Red Cross and the American Heart Association are nonprofit organizations.

_____ **4.** The law of supply states that businesses will provide fewer products when they must sell them at lower prices.

_____ **5.** Some monopolies are legal.

_____ **6.** Capitalism encourages people to work and to invest.

_____ **7.** The word *labor* is often used to mean workers as opposed to owners and people who manage companies.

_____ **8.** A natural resource is considered a factor of production only when it is plentiful.

_____ **9.** Examples of capital are trucks, machines, and office equipment.

_____ **10.** Businesses must often raise their prices to cover the costs of meeting government regulations.

_____ **11.** Every business enterprise needs land.

Chapter 17, Test Form C, continued

IDENTIFICATION *(3 points each)* Place the steps below in the proper order to show how a business works.

   a. entrepreneur raises capital
   b. entrepreneur buys land and natural resources needed
   c. stockholders earn dividends
   d. entrepreneur wants to start business
   e. business makes profit
   f. stockholders elect board of directors
   g. entrepreneur sets up business as a corporation

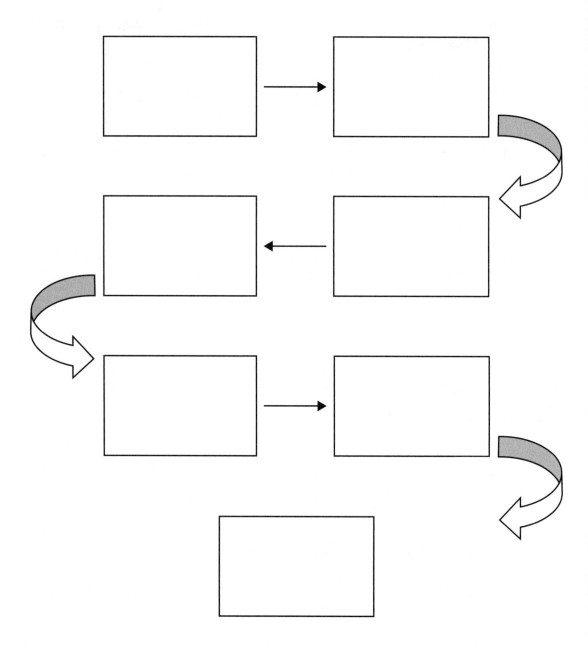

Chapter Test Form C

Goods and Services

MATCHING *(3 points each)* Place the letters of the descriptions next to the appropriate terms.

_____ **1.** consumer

_____ **2.** shoplifting

_____ **3.** charge account

_____ **4.** credit rating

_____ **5.** down payment

_____ **6.** gross domestic product

_____ **7.** balance

_____ **8.** mass production

_____ **9.** installments

_____ **10.** distribution

a. the cash used to pay part of the purchase price

b. stealing items displayed in stores

c. a person who buys or uses goods and services

d. equal payments

e. a form of credit that stores grant to many of their customers

f. the rest of what a buyer owes the seller

g. the rapid production by machine of large numbers of identical objects

h. the dollar value of all goods and services produced annually in the United States

i. the process of moving goods from manufacturers to people who want them

j. based on a report that shows how reliable a customer is in paying bills

FILL IN THE BLANK *(3 points each)* Choose the correct items from the following list to complete the statements below.

machine tools	assembly line	self-service
interchangeable parts	division of labor	
standard packaging	advertising	

1. In _____, each worker is responsible for a specific task in production.

2. _____ are machinery built to produce parts that are exactly the same.

3. _____ is an efficient and inexpensive way to sell goods because it saves time and labor.

4. _____ informs people about products and tries to persuade them to buy these products.

5. _____ means that goods come from factories already wrapped.

Chapter 18, Test Form C, continued

6. A(n) _____ uses machines and workers to move a product through stages of production until it is completed.

7. _____ allows every part of a product to fit any other part.

TRUE/FALSE *(2 points each)* Mark each statement *T* if it is true or *F* if it is false.

_____ **1.** The source of power that contributed most to modern mass production was waterpower.

_____ **2.** Mass production was first developed in England.

_____ **3.** Cuba uses mass-production methods but has not been as successful as other countries due to its command economy.

_____ **4.** U.S. trains are faster than trains in other countries.

_____ **5.** A factory often sells goods to a wholesaler who then sells them to retailers.

_____ **6.** A chain store is owned and operated by a company that has many of the same kind of stores.

_____ **7.** Anyone can open a charge account, regardless of his or her past credit history.

_____ **8.** Some laws require products to show unit pricing on their label.

_____ **9.** Shoplifting can eventually cause consumers to pay more for products and services.

_____ **10.** If a customer makes late or incomplete payments on a product, the seller can repossess the item.

_____ **11.** Shoplifting hardly hurts a business.

Name _____ Class _____ Date _____

IDENTIFICATION *(3 points each)* Place the steps below in the proper order to show the "life" of a product. Fill in the options or subcategories of each major step in the circles on either side. (Hint: The words in bold indicate the steps. You should put the letters for those words in the boxes.)

a. division of labor
b. transportation
c. distribution
d. mass production
e. purchases
f. marketing
g. assembly lines
h. charge account
i. cash

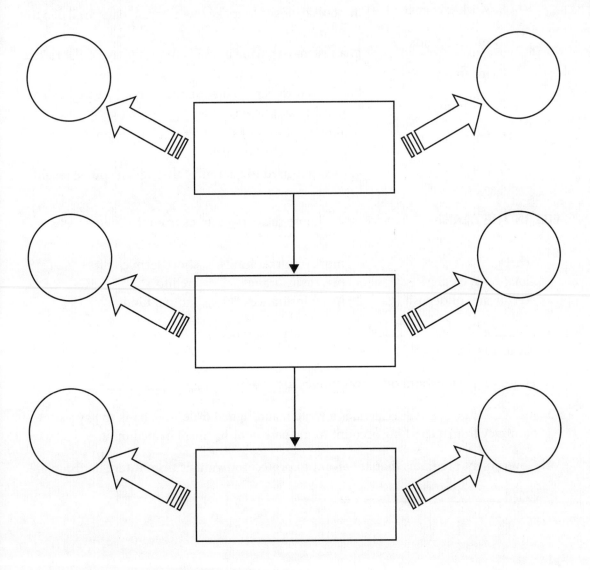

CHAPTER **19**

Chapter Test Form C

Managing Money

MATCHING *(3 points each)* Place the letters of the descriptions next to the appropriate terms.

_____ **1.** currency

_____ **2.** credit card

_____ **3.** bankruptcy

_____ **4.** collateral

_____ **5.** credit union

_____ **6.** stock exchange

_____ **7.** mutual funds

_____ **8.** insurance

_____ **9.** premium

_____ **10.** Social Security

a. a legal declaration that a person cannot pay his or her debts

b. composed of many different stocks, making it a relatively low-risk investment

c. the small amount a person pays for insurance

d. coins and paper money

e. provides old-age insurance, unemployment insurance, and workers' compensation

f. pools deposits to make low-interest loans available to members

g. a system of paying a small amount to avoid the risk of a large loss

h. allow customers to buy things without paying cash at the time of purchase

i. allows millions of shares of stock to be bought and sold every working day

j. property used to guarantee that a loan will be repaid

FILL IN THE BLANK *(3 points each)* Choose the correct items from the following list to complete the statements below.

check	money market funds	short-term credit
long-term credit	private insurance	creditors
certificates of deposit (CD)	social insurance	mutual funds

1. _____ is a voluntary insurance that individuals and companies pay to cover unexpected losses.

2. Those people to whom one owes money are called _____.

3. A _____ is a written and signed order to a bank to pay a sum of money from a checking account to the person or business named on it.

4. Government programs that are meant to protect individuals from future hardship are

called _____.

Chapter 19, Test Form C, continued

5. _____ buy stocks that most individuals could not purchase alone and allow individuals to withdraw their money at any time.

6. If you purchase an item on credit and can repay the debt in a few weeks or months, you need only _____.

7. _____ allow savers to invest a certain amount of money for a specified period of time during which time the money cannot be withdrawn.

8. _____ is also called installment credit.

9. _____ contain many different stocks so that the risk is not so great.

TRUE/FALSE *(2 points each)* Mark each statement *T* if it is true or *F* if it is false.

_____ **1.** Today a nickel is still made of pure nickel.

_____ **2.** All currency must be easy to carry and take up little space.

_____ **3.** To slow consumer spending, banks may extend less credit to customers when production drops.

_____ **4.** Most of what is bought and sold in the United States is paid for with coins and paper money.

_____ **5.** The Federal Reserve System requires that all U.S. banks meet its requirements.

_____ **6.** FDIC insures the amount of money a depositor has in the bank.

_____ **7.** By law, banks cannot turn down a person who seeks a loan from them.

_____ **8.** If the Federal Reserve wants to speed economic growth, it puts more money into circulation.

_____ **9.** Stock prices depend on expectations of how well a company will perform in the future.

_____ **10.** When you invest, you turn your money into capital.

_____ **11.** Certificates of deposit allow the holder to withdraw money at any time.

Chapter 19, Test Form C, continued

IDENTIFICATION *(3 points each)* Imagine that you have just received a paycheck for work you have done. You have many options in terms of what you may do with the money. Fill in the diagram below with the proper terms to illustrate your various options.

a. check
b. bank
c. invest
d. debit card
e. money market account
f. mutual funds
g. credit card

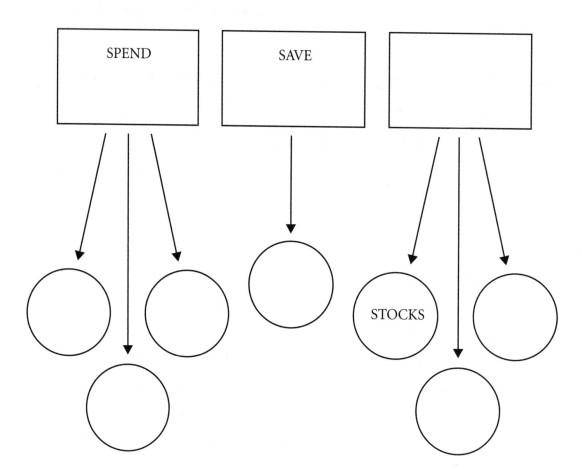

Chapter Test Form C

Economic Challenges

MATCHING *(3 points each)* Place the letters of the descriptions next to the appropriate terms.

_____ **1.** fiscal policy

_____ **2.** monetary policy

_____ **3.** union shop

_____ **4.** agency shop

_____ **5.** right-to-work laws

_____ **6.** featherbedding

_____ **7.** mediation

_____ **8.** arbitration

_____ **9.** business cycle

_____ **10.** expansion

a. process in which the economy goes from good times to bad and then back to good times again

b. an employer can hire any qualified worker, union or nonunion

c. when a union forces employers to hire more workers than needed

d. period of growth for the economy

e. a law that dictates no one may be forced to join a union

f. federal government's policy regarding money

g. recommendations of a mediator are binding on both sides

h. the federal government's policy of taxing and spending

i. an expert on relations between labor and management may be asked to examine a conflict and recommend a solution

j. a worker cannot be forced to join a union, but must pay union dues

FILL IN THE BLANK *(3 points each)* Choose the correct items from the following list to complete the statements below.

inflation	trough	job action
costs of production	labor unions	blacklists
contraction	collective bargaining	lockouts

1. Organizations of workers hoping to improve wages and working conditions are called

_____.

2. _____ prevent workers from earning wages by closing the factory.

3. Wages, payments for raw materials, and rent are called the

_____.

4. An economic slowdown is referred to as a(n) _____.

Chapter 20, Test Form C, *continued*

5. _____ contained names of workers who were active in the labor unions, indicating to other companies that they were not to hire these workers.

6. Any kind of slowdown, or action short of a strike, is called a(n)

_____.

7. In _____, representatives of a labor union meet with representatives of an employer to reach an agreement.

8. _____ refers to a rise in the costs of goods and services.

9. When the economy reaches its lowest point, it is said to be in a(n)

_____.

TRUE/FALSE *(2 points each)* Mark each statement *T* if it is true or *F* if it is false.

_____ **1.** The business cycle is common to free-market economies.

_____ **2.** Before the Great Depression, many economists believed that the government should intervene in the business cycle.

_____ **3.** Unemployment helps the economy to prosper.

_____ **4.** When inflation becomes too high, the government may reduce its spending.

_____ **5.** If the total amount produced each hour increases, the supply of goods increases.

_____ **6.** Because only about 14.9 percent of workers are union members, the American labor unions are weak.

_____ **7.** In the first half of the 1800s, factories employed young children as workers.

_____ **8.** When workers go on strike, the only people they affect are their employers.

_____ **9.** In the early days of the country, most Americans were employed by factories.

_____**10.** During expansion, the cost of doing business increases.

_____**11.** The Great Depression lasted about a year.

Name _____ Class _____ Date _____

IDENTIFICATION *(3 points each)* Certain factors increase or decrease within an
expansion or contraction. Place each letter into the correct box.

  a. GDP increases.
  b. GDP decreases.
  c. Unemployment increases.
  d. Unemployment decreases.
  e. Demand for goods increases.
  f. Demand for goods decreases.
  g. Inflation increases.

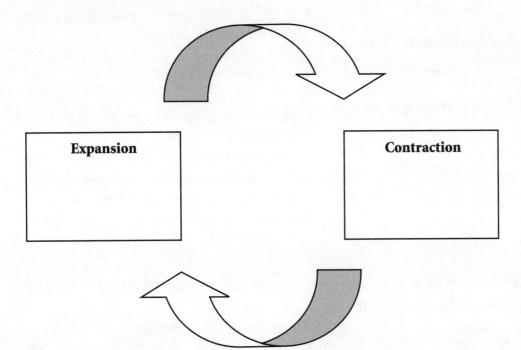

CHAPTER **21**   Chapter Test Form C

The U.S. Economy and the World

MATCHING *(3 points each)* Place the letters of the descriptions next to the appropriate terms.

_____ **1.** competition

_____ **2.** surplus

_____ **3.** shortage

_____ **4.** stock

_____ **5.** leading indicators

_____ **6.** coincident indicators

_____ **7.** import quota

_____ **8.** embargo

_____ **9.** protectionism

_____ **10.** free trade

a. signs that help economists make predictions about future economic growth

b. bans imports from specific countries

c. international trade without any government regulation

d. occurs when the quantity demanded is greater than the quantity supplied

e. a law that limits the amount or number of a certain import

f. the use of protective tariffs between countries

g. occurs when the quantity supplied is greater than the quantity demanded

h. represents ownership in a business

i. the economic rivalry that exists among businesses selling products that are similar

j. signs that show economists how the economy is doing at the present time

FILL IN THE BLANK *(3 points each)* Choose the correct items from the following list to complete the statements below.

producer	circular-flow model	supply
tax incentive	open-market operations	trade barrier
easy-money policy	opportunity cost	comparative advantage

1. The _____ demonstrates how the U.S. economy works.

2. Economists determine a(n) _____ by figuring out which product or service offers each country that greatest absolute advantage.

3. A person or company that produces a good or service that satisfies consumers' needs and wants is called a(n) _____.

4. A government action that limits the exchange of goods is called a(n)

_____.

5. _____ is the quantity of goods and services that producers are willing to offer at various possible prices during a given time period.

6. A(n) _____ is a special tax break.

7. _____ may be defined as the value of the alternative that has been sacrificed during a trade-off.

8. A(n)_____ increases the amount of money in the money supply.

9. _____ is defined as the buying and selling of government securities.

TRUE/FALSE *(2 points each)* Mark each statement *T* if it is true or *F* if it is false.

_____ **1.** A shortage indicates to producers that they are charging too much for their product.

_____ **2.** The U.S. government does not play a role in the U.S. economy.

_____ **3.** Lagging indicators change immediately after an upturn or downturn in the economy has started.

_____ **4.** Individuals and businesses generally borrow money when interest rates are low.

_____ **5.** Declining investment makes it more likely that the economy will expand.

_____ **6.** To reduce unemployment, the government can reduce its spending.

_____ **7.** Negative side effects of economic activities may include pollution and traffic jams.

_____ **8.** The effects of fiscal policy are usually seen immediately.

_____ **9.** Most countries do not support international trade.

_____ **10.** Many countries are fully self-sufficient.

_____ **11.** The United States still has an embargo on South Africa.

_____ **12.** Competition does not benefit producers in any way.

_____ **13.** It is cheaper to produce goods in the United States than in any other country.

_____ **14.** The events of September 11, 2001, harmed the U.S. economy.

Chapter 21, Test Form C, continued

IDENTIFICATION *(3 points each)* Place the steps below in the proper order to show the "life" of a product. Fill in the options or subcategories of each major step in the circles on either side.

    a. The government increases tax incentives.
    b. The economy expands.
    c. The economy slows.
    d. The Fed raises reserve requirement.

CAUSE   **EFFECT**

Fed lowers discount rate.   _____

_____   **The economy slows.**

An easy-money policy is enacted.   _____

The government raises taxes.   _____

_____   **The economy expands.**

CHAPTER **22**

Chapter Test Form C

Career Choices

MATCHING *(3 points each)* Place the letters of the descriptions next to the appropriate terms.

_____ **1.** personal values

_____ **2.** qualifications

_____ **3.** white-collar workers

_____ **4.** professionals

_____ **5.** technicians

_____ **6.** blue-collar workers

_____ **7.** equal opportunity employer

_____ **8.** salary range

_____ **9.** motor skills

_____ **10.** perceptual skills

a. people who work in a particular profession or who perform technical, managerial, sales, or administrative support work

b. workers who perform jobs that require manual labor

c. beginning salary, possible raises, and highest salary

d. people who perform jobs that require some specialized skill in addition to a solid, basic education

e. how well people can use their hands

f. the skills and knowledge a person has

g. an employer does not discriminate against job applicants because of their sex, age, race, skin color, religion, or ethnic background

h. people who work at jobs that require many years of education and training, and in which the work tends to be mental rather than physical

i. the ability to picture things in your mind

j. the things people believe to be the most important in their lives

FILL IN THE BLANK *(3 points each)* Choose the correct items from the following list to complete the statements below.

automation   interpersonal skills
laborers   aptitude tests
operators   agribusinesses

1. People who run machines or equipment in factories, mills, industrial plants, gas

stations, mines, and laundries are called _____.

2. _____, or skills in handling personal relationships, are important in teaching and sales.

3. _____ may be defined as the use of machines instead of workers to provide goods and services.

Chapter 22, Test Form C, continued

4. Workers who perform heavy physical work are called _____.

5. _____ are large farms owned by corporations that rely heavily on mechanized equipment.

6. Interest tests are also called _____.

TRUE/FALSE *(2 points each)* Mark each statement *T* if it is true or *F* if it is false.

_____ **1.** The country's largest employer is the U.S. government.

_____ **2.** The government tells U.S. citizens what profession they ought to pursue.

_____ **3.** Every 10 years, the U.S. Department of Labor reports where men and women are working and what jobs they are performing.

_____ **4.** Truck and bus drivers are considered operators.

_____ **5.** There is nothing you can do at your age to prepare for a career.

_____ **6.** It is wise to focus on and develop skills in only one area.

_____ **7.** Today 1 in every 200 employed Americans is a service worker.

_____ **8.** Before a candidate is offered a government job, he or she must be subject to an extensive background check.

_____ **9.** Some people choose a career solely because they can earn a high income.

_____ **10.** Members of the Equal Employment Opportunity Commission are elected by citizens.

_____ **11.** A dental hygienist is an example of a sales worker.

_____ **12.** An employer expects that his or her employees know everything about a place of business before the employee even begins.

_____ **13.** Most jobs in the military are now open to women.

_____ **14.** Law-enforcement officers and teachers are always in demand.

Chapter 22, Test Form C, continued

IDENTIFICATION *(3 points each)* Fill in the chart below by placing the terms in their appropriate places.

    a. nursing assistants
    b. craftspersons
    c. firefighters
    d. professionals
    e. blue-collar workers
    f. technicians
    g. farmers
    h. operators

Examples of Workers

White-Collar Workers		Service Workers	Agricultural Workers

UNIT 6

Test Form C

The American Economy

MATCHING *(3 points each)* In the space provided, write the letter of the term that matches each description. Choose your answers from the list below.

_____ **1.** patent

_____ **2.** gross income

_____ **3.** gross domestic product

_____ **4.** consumer

_____ **5.** bankruptcy

_____ **6.** insurance

_____ **7.** expansion

_____ **8.** right-to-work laws

_____ **9.** opportunity cost

_____ **10.** motor skills

a. a legal declaration that a person cannot pay his or her debts

b. period of growth for the economy

c. a person who buys or uses goods and services

d. how well people can use their hands

e. money left over after all costs have been paid

f. the value of the alternative that has been sacrificed during a trade-off

g. a law that dictates no one may be forced to join a union

h. allows a person the exclusive right to create and sell an invention for a certain number of years

i. a system of paying a small amount to avoid the risk of a large loss

j. the dollar value of all goods and services produced annually in the United States

FILL IN THE BLANK *(3 points each)* Choose from the following list to complete each of the statements below.

market economy	competition	agribusinesses
certificates of deposit (CD)	inflation	
advertising	creditors	

1. _____ allow savers to invest a certain amount of money, which cannot be withdrawn for a specified period of time.

2. An economy in which people have the freedom to buy and sell what they want when they choose is called a(n)_____ .

3. _____ informs people about products and tries to persuade them to buy these products.

4. People to whom one owes money are called _____.

5. _____ refers to a rise in the costs of goods and services.

Unit 6, Test Form C, continued

6. _____ is the economic rivalry that exists among businesses selling similar products.

7. _____ are large farms owned by corporations that rely heavily on mechanized equipment.

TRUE/FALSE *(2 points each)* Mark each statement *T* if it is true or *F* if it is false.

_____ **1.** The American Red Cross and the American Heart Association are nonprofit organizations.

_____ **2.** Examples of capital include trucks, machines, and office equipment.

_____ **3.** Capitalism encourages people to work and to invest their money.

_____ **4.** U.S. trains operate at faster speeds than trains in other countries.

_____ **5.** Some laws require that products show their unit pricing on the label.

_____ **6.** Shoplifting hardly hurts a business.

_____ **7.** Demand is the quantity of goods and services that producers are willing to offer at various prices during a given time period.

_____ **8.** The Federal Reserve System requires that all U.S. banks meet its requirements.

_____ **9.** Unemployment helps the economy to prosper.

_____ **10.** When workers go on strike, the only people they affect are their employers.

_____ **11.** Fiscal policy usually has long-term effects on the economy.

_____ **12.** Every 10 years the U.S. Department of Labor reports where men and women are working and what jobs they are performing.

_____ **13.** Before a candidate is offered a government job, he or she will undergo an extensive background check.

_____ **14.** Law-enforcement officers and teachers are always in demand.

Unit 6, Test Form C, continued

IDENTIFICATION *(3 points each)* In a typical business cycle, certain factors increase or decrease within an expansion or contraction of the economy. Write the letters of each description in the box that corresponds to an expansion or contraction.

  a. GDP increases.
  b. GDP decreases.
  c. Unemployment increases.
  d. Unemployment decreases.
  e. Spending increases.
  f. Demand for goods decreases.
  g. Inflation increases.

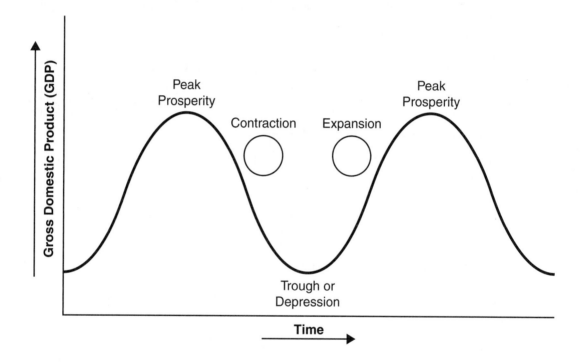

Chapter Test Form C

Foreign Policy

MATCHING *(3 points each)* Place the letters of the descriptions next to the appropriate terms.

_____ **1.** interdependence

_____ **2.** alliances

_____ **3.** executive agreement

_____ **4.** summit

_____ **5.** foreign aid

_____ **6.** newly industrialized countries

_____ **7.** balance of trade

_____ **8.** United Nations

_____ **9.** General Assembly

_____ **10.** Security Council

a. a meeting between leaders of two or more countries to discuss issues that concern those countries

b. have experienced rapid industrialization and economic growth in recent years

c. mutual reliance

d. the UN body that discusses, debates, and recommends solutions to problems

e. an organization that promotes peaceful coexistence and worldwide cooperation

f. any government program that provides economic or military assistance to another country

g. the difference in the value between a country's exports and imports over a period of time

h. the UN body responsible for peacekeeping

i. countries that agree to help each other for defense, economic, scientific, or other reasons

j. mutual understanding between the leaders of two countries

FILL IN THE BLANK *(3 points each)* Choose the correct items from the following list to complete the statements below.

diplomatic recognition   exports   free trade
diplomatic corps   imports   International Court of Justice
couriers   trade deficits

1. _____ is trade that is not restricted by tariffs and other trade barriers.

2. U.S. ambassadors, ministers, and consuls are members of the

_____ .

3. _____ are those goods and services that the United States buys from other countries.

4. _____ are special messengers that transport important reports.

Chapter 23, Test Form C, continued

5. _____ are those goods and services that the United States sells to other countries.

6. The _____ is also known as the World Court.

7. _____ occur when the country spends more money buying imports than it earns from selling exports to other countries.

8. _____ means that the president may decide whether to recognize the government of a foreign country.

TRUE/FALSE *(2 points each)* Mark each statement *T* if it is true or *F* if it is false.

_____ **1.** The Secretariat has nearly 9,000 staff members.

_____ **2.** The World Health Organization extends educational opportunities everywhere in the world.

_____ **3.** All important issues must be agreed on by a two-thirds majority in the General Assembly.

_____ **4.** The United States first gave large amounts of foreign aid during World War II.

_____ **5.** The United States does not have an alliance with Japan or South Korea.

_____ **6.** The United States refused to sign the North American Free Trade Agreement (NAFTA).

_____ **7.** All spending for national defense must be approved by Congress.

_____ **8.** The president does not need approval from the Senate to appoint ambassadors to represent the United States in foreign countries.

_____ **9.** Members of the National Security Council include the president, vice president, and the secretaries of defense, state, and the treasury.

_____ **10.** Only Congress can declare war.

_____ **11.** The Security Council includes one member from every country involved in the UN.

_____ **12.** The Atlantic Charter dictated that no country should try to gain territory as a result of war.

_____ **13.** UN peacekeepers are authorized to use force in settling disputes only in extremely dangerous situations.

_____ **14.** Each specialized agency is independent of the main UN body.

IDENTIFICATION *(3 points each)* Fill in the chart with the lettered terms from the following list.

  a. United Nations
  b. North Atlantic Treaty Organization
  c. organization that promotes peaceful coexistence and worldwide cooperation
  d. allows free trade between the United States, Canada, and Mexico
  e. establish a united front against aggression by communists
  f. NAFTA

ACRONYM	NAME OF ORGANIZATION	JOB OF ORGANIZATION
NATO		
	North American Free Trade Agreement	
UN		

Chapter Test Form C

Charting a Course

MATCHING *(3 points each)* Place the letters of the descriptions next to the appropriate terms.

_____ **1.** isolationism

_____ **2.** dollar diplomacy

_____ **3.** communism

_____ **4.** Pentagon

_____ **5.** War on Drugs

_____ **6.** containment

_____ **7.** détente

_____ **8.** apartheid

_____ **9.** the Cold War

_____ **10.** Taliban

a. headquarters of the U.S. military leadership

b. U.S. foreign policy in Latin America

c. world competition for global power and influence

d. organized effort to end the trade and use of illegal drugs

e. an economic system in which the working class takes over factories and businesses, thereby preventing any group from owning all of the means of production

f. separation of races

g. U.S. policy that prevented Soviet communism from spreading to other countries

h. dictates that the United States should avoid involvement in all foreign affairs

i. the ruling government in Afghanistan driven from power in 2002

j. lessening of tensions

FILL IN THE BLANK *(3 points each)* Choose the correct items from the following list to complete the statements below.

doctrine	satellite nations	terrorists
corollary	limited war	balance of power
neutrality	perestroika	glasnost

1. _____ are those countries that are controlled by another country.

2. A _____ is a statement that follows as a natural or logical result.

3. A situation in which countries are about equal in strength is called a

_____ .

Chapter 24, Test Form C, continued

4. _____ means restructuring.

5. If a country adopts a policy of _____, then it does not assist or favor either side in a disagreement.

6. Individuals who use violence to achieve political goals are called

_____.

7. Gorbachev introduced a policy called _____ aimed at giving the Soviet people more freedom.

8. A _____ sets forth a new way of interacting with other countries.

9. A _____ is fought without using a country's full power, such as nuclear weapons.

TRUE/FALSE *(2 points each)* Mark each statement *T* if it is true or *F* if it is false.

_____ **1.** In 1917 China became the first country to adopt a communist system.

_____ **2.** Fidel Castro set up a communist government in Cuba in 1959.

_____ **3.** During the Cuban missile crisis, the United States tried to prevent the delivery of weapons to Cuba.

_____ **4.** The War of 1812 ended in a stalemate.

_____ **5.** The United States stayed neutral throughout World Wars I and II.

_____ **6.** Many senators opposed U.S. membership in the League of Nations.

_____ **7.** The Cold War is still a major problem.

_____ **8.** President George W. Bush created the Office of Homeland Security after the terrorist attacks of September 11, 2001.

_____ **9.** India and Pakistan have fought three wars since the two countries won their independence from Great Britain.

_____ **10.** An embargo, or government order against trade, between the United States and Cuba is no longer in effect.

_____ **11.** Foreign policies hardly ever change.

Name _____ Class _____ Date _____

IDENTIFICATION *(3 points each)* Put the following events in their appropriate places on the time line.
  a. Cuban missile crisis
  b. Vietnam
  c. terrorist attacks on World Trade Center
  d. Korean War
  e. World War II
  f. fall of Berlin Wall

1940   1950   1960   1970   1980   1990   2000   2010

☐   ☐   ☐   ☐   ☐   ☐

Name _____ Class _____ Date _____

 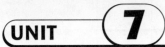
MATCHING *(3 points each)* Write the letters of the descriptions next to the appropriate terms.

_____ **1.** summit

_____ **2.** isolationism

_____ **3.** newly industrial-
            ized countries

_____ **4.** communism

_____ **5.** interdependence

_____ **6.** apartheid

_____ **7.** containment

_____ **8.** United Nations

_____ **9.** Taliban

_____**10.** alliances

a. an economic system in which the working class takes over factories and businesses, thereby preventing any group from owning all the means of production

b. prevented Soviet communism from spreading to other countries

c. have experienced rapid industrialization and economic growth in recent years

d. a meeting between leaders of two or more countries to discuss issues that concern those countries

e. result when countries agree to help each other for defense, economic, scientific, or other reasons

f. an organization that promotes peaceful coexistence and worldwide cooperation

g. separation of races

h. mutual reliance

i. dictates that a country should avoid involvement in all foreign affairs

j. Afghanistan's ruling government that was driven from power in 2002

FILL IN THE BLANK *(3 points each)* Choose from the following list to complete each of the statements below.

diplomatic recognition   exports   free trade
diplomatic corps   imports   balance of power
neutrality   perestroika   doctrine

1. _____ are those goods and services that the United States sells to other countries.

2. A(n) _____ sets forth a new way of interacting with other countries.

3. _____ is trade that is not restricted by tariffs and other trade barriers.

Unit 7, Test Form C, continued

4. A situation in which countries are about equal in strength is called a(n)

_____.

5. _____ means that the president may decide whether to recognize the government of a foreign country.

6. U.S. ambassadors, ministers, and consuls are members of the

_____.

7. _____ are those goods and services that the United States buys from other countries.

8. _____ means restructuring.

9. If a country adopts a policy of _____, then it does not assist or favor either side in a disagreement.

TRUE/FALSE *(2 points each)* Mark each statement *T* if it is true or *F* if it is false.

_____ **1.** The World Health Organization extends educational opportunities everywhere in the world.

_____ **2.** The United States does not have an alliance with Japan or South Korea.

_____ **3.** All spending for national defense must be approved by Congress.

_____ **4.** Only Congress can declare war.

_____ **5.** UN peacekeepers are authorized to use their weapons only in self-defense.

_____ **6.** The United States stayed neutral throughout World Wars I and II.

_____ **7.** Fidel Castro set up a communist government in Cuba in 1959.

_____ **8.** President George W. Bush created the Office of Homeland Security after the terrorist attacks of September 11, 2001.

_____ **9.** Many senators opposed U.S. membership in the League of Nations.

_____**10.** Foreign policies hardly ever change.

_____**11.** During the Cuban missile crisis, the United States refused to allow weapons to be delivered to Cuba.

IDENTIFICATION *(3 points each)* Place the letter of the correct word or phrase into its proper place below to show the hierarchy of courts and their characteristics.

  a. laws created by government agencies

  b. administrative law

  c. someone driving a car too fast is held responsible, even though there are no rules governing a speed limit

  d. Congress and state and local governments pass these laws

  e. law based on the Constitution and on Supreme Court decisions

  f. common law

  g. a state law that requires fire exits in all public buildings

Type of Law	Definition	Example
statutory law		
		Consumer Product Safety commission makes a law that rules a particular toy is unsafe
	based on certain rules that we have accepted as the proper way in which to act	
constitutional law		

Chapter Test Form C

Improving Life for All Americans

MATCHING *(3 points each)* Place the letters of the descriptions next to the appropriate terms.

_____ **1.** public housing projects

_____ **2.** urban-renewal programs

_____ **3.** homelessness

_____ **4.** minority groups

_____ **5.** discrimination

_____ **6.** ethnic groups

_____ **7.** civil rights movement

_____ **8.** drug abuse

_____ **9.** addict

_____ **10.** alcoholism

a. improve neglected neighborhoods and restore and maintain buildings in a particular area

b. refers to unfair actions taken against people because they belong to a particular group

c. people who supported this opposed laws that denied equal rights to African Americans and others

d. do not have as much political or economic power as other groups

e. a person who feels the compulsive need to do something

f. a major social problem that affects 750,000 people today

g. consist of people of the same race, nationality, or religion who share a common, distinctive culture and heritage

h. apartment buildings built with public funds

i. the continued excessive use of alcohol

j. using drugs for recreation

FILL IN THE BLANK *(3 points each)* Choose the correct items from the following list to complete the statements below.

zoning laws   boycott   civil disobedience
building codes   dissent
mass transit   demonstration

1. _____ means disagreement.

2. _____ dictate that buildings be inspected regularly.

3. During a _____, dissenters march in public carrying signs, singing songs, and making speeches.

Chapter 25, Test Form C, continued

4. A _____ calls for people to stop using a particular product or service.

5. Intentionally disobeying laws that people believe are wrong is called

_____.

6. _____ regulate the kinds of buildings and businesses that may be located in a certain area.

7. _____ includes various forms of public transportation, such as subways, buses, and commuter railroads.

TRUE/FALSE *(2 points each)* Mark each statement *T* if it is true or *F* if it is false.

_____ **1.** Hispanics form one of the smallest and slowest-growing minority groups in the United States.

_____ **2.** Martin Luther King Jr. was a major leader in the civil rights movement.

_____ **3.** Drugs prescribed by physicians are harmless.

_____ **4.** Smoking only poses a threat to smokers and not to nonsmokers.

_____ **5.** People who contract AIDS become sick immediately.

_____ **6.** Smoke detectors are not effective for warning of a fire in the home.

_____ **7.** Cities today are usually divided into two parts—the older, central part of the city and the suburbs.

_____ **8.** More and more people are using mass transit today.

_____ **9.** Many homeless people are unable to get jobs because they have no permanent address and phone number.

_____**10.** During the mid- to late 1900s, the centers of American cities began losing population.

_____**11.** Urban-renewal programs usually receive financial support from the federal government.

Chapter 25, Test Form C, continued

IDENTIFICATION *(3 points each)* Fill in the diagram below to illustrate the food chain.
  a. Plants and trees grow.
  b. Bacteria eat dead leaves.
  c. Soil is enriched.
  d. Leaves decay.
  e. Animals eat plants and trees.

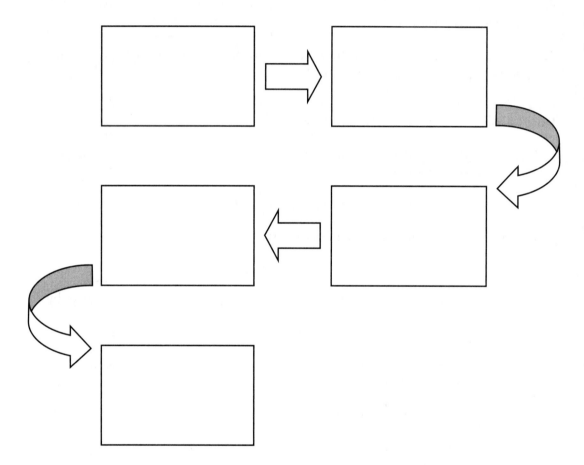

CHAPTER **26**

Chapter Test Form C

The Global Environment

MATCHING *(3 points each)* Write the letters of the descriptions next to the appropriate terms.

_____ **1.** nonrenewable resources

_____ **2.** fossil fuels

_____ **3.** conservation

_____ **4.** strip mining

_____ **5.** biomass

_____ **6.** Endangered Species Acts

_____ **7.** Environmental Protection Agency

_____ **8.** Earth Day

_____ **9.** ecology

_____ **10.** fertilizers

a. removing top layers of soil to reach coal deposits

b. those resources that can be used only once

c. protect species that are close to extinction

d. energy source that consists of wood and waste products

e. plant foods that make crops grow faster and bigger

f. organization of federal bureaus that deal with pollution and other environmental issues

g. petroleum, natural gas, and coal

h. an unofficial holiday dedicated to caring for Earth

i. the study of all living things in relation to each other and to their environment

j. refers to safeguarding natural resources by using them wisely

FILL IN THE BLANK *(3 points each)* Choose the correct items from the following list to complete the statements below.

erosion	desertification	organic farming
ecosystem	pesticides	landfills
smog	acid rain	recycling

1. A combination of smoke, gases, and fog is called _____.

2. _____ are huge pits dug in the ground that are used to store large amounts of garbage.

3. _____ are chemicals that kill insect pests and weeds.

4. _____ is a process that occurs when years of overgrazing and removal of plants harm the soil, and once-fertile areas become deserts.

Chapter 26, Test Form C, continued

5. _____ occurs when pollution from burning gas, oil, and coal mixes with water vapor to form acid.

6. _____ is defined as the wearing away of land by water and wind.

7. _____ is the process of turning waste into something that can be used again.

8. _____ does not include the use of artificial substances.

9. A(n) _____ is a community of interdependent living things existing in balance with their physical environment.

TRUE/FALSE *(2 points each)* Mark each statement *T* if it is true or *F* if it is false.

_____ **1.** The explosion at Chernobyl affected only the people who were in the plant at the time.

_____ **2.** Petroleum can be used to create a wide variety of products, such as plastics, pesticides, and many chemicals.

_____ **3.** The world's supply of oil is unlimited.

_____ **4.** Most people support the use of nuclear energy.

_____ **5.** Federal, state, and local laws cannot guarantee that the environment will be protected.

_____ **6.** The National Park Service is the only agency that helps preserve the natural resources of the United States.

_____ **7.** Early settlers did not have enough trees and forests for their needs.

_____ **8.** All living things depend on each other for survival.

_____ **9.** All farmers have stopped using fertilizers and pesticides.

_____ **10.** As land is farmed year after year, it becomes more fertile.

_____ **11.** Solar energy is a very promising source of alternative energy.

_____ **12.** Coal is the most plentiful fossil fuel, and it is renewable.

_____ **13.** Strip mining is an effective and harmless way of getting coal.

_____ **14.** Natural gas is the cleanest-burning fossil fuel.

Name _____ Class _____ Date _____

IDENTIFICATION *(3 points each)* Fill in the chart below.
- **a.** ozone layer depletion
- **b.** ground pollution
- **c.** water pollution and water shortages
- **d.** use solar, wind, or biomass power
- **e.** do not litter in oceans, lakes, and rivers

ENVIRONMENTAL PROBLEMS	POSSIBLE SOLUTIONS
1.	**RECYCLE**
FOSSIL FUEL SHORTAGE	**2.**
WATER POLLUTION	**3.**
4.	**BAN CFCS**
5.	**CONSERVE WATER**

UNIT 8

Test Form C

Meeting Future Challenges

MATCHING *(3 points each)* Place the letters of the descriptions next to the appropriate terms.

_____ **1.** public housing projects

_____ **2.** urban-renewal programs

_____ **3.** homelessness

_____ **4.** minority groups

_____ **5.** discrimination

_____ **6.** nonrenewable resources

_____ **7.** fossil fuels

_____ **8.** conservation

_____ **9.** strip mining

_____ **10.** biomass

a. refers to unfair actions taken against people because they belong to a particular group

b. refers to the safeguarding of natural resources by using them wisely

c. removing top layers of soil to reach coal deposits

d. a major social problem that affects 750,000 people today

e. energy sources that consist of wood and waste products

f. petroleum, natural gas, and coal

g. apartment buildings built with public funds

h. those resources that can be used only once

i. do not have as much political or economic power as other groups

j. improve neglected neighborhoods and restore and maintain buildings in a particular area

FILL IN THE BLANK *(3 points each)* Choose from the following list to complete each of the statements below.

zoning laws	boycott	civil disobedience
building codes	dissent	landfills
smog	acid rain	recycling

1. _____ regulate the kinds of buildings and businesses that may be located in a certain area.

2. A combination of smoke, gases, and fog is called _____.

3. _____ is the process of turning waste into something that can be used again.

4. Intentionally disobeying laws that one believes are wrong is called

_____.

5. _____ occurs when pollution from burning gas, oil, and coal mixes with water vapor to form acid.

Unit 8, Test Form C, continued

6. _____ are huge pits dug in the ground in order to store large amounts of garbage.

7. _____ dictate that buildings be inspected regularly.

8. A(n) _____ calls for people to stop using a particular product or service.

9. _____ means disagreement.

TRUE/FALSE *(2 points each)* Mark each statement *T* if it is true or *F* if it is false.

_____ **1.** Smoking poses a threat to smokers but not to nonsmokers.

_____ **2.** Typically, cities today are divided into two parts—the older, central part of the city and the suburbs.

_____ **3.** Most people support the use of nuclear energy.

_____ **4.** All farmers have stopped using fertilizers and pesticides.

_____ **5.** Drugs prescribed by physicians are harmless.

_____ **6.** During the mid- to late 1900s, the centers of American cities began losing population.

_____ **7.** Natural gas is the cleanest-burning fossil fuel.

_____ **8.** Solar energy is a very promising source of alternative energy.

_____ **9.** Martin Luther King Jr. was a major leader in the civil rights movement.

_____ **10.** Hispanics form one of the smallest and slowest-growing minority groups in the United States.

_____ **11.** Strip mining is an effective and harmless way of getting coal.

IDENTIFICATION *(3 points each)* Place the letter of the correct word or phrase into its proper place in the diagram below.

a. lower courts

b. attorney general

c. the House of Representatives

d. appeals courts

e. lieutenant governor

f. state supreme court

g. secretary of state

h. general trial courts

i. the Senate

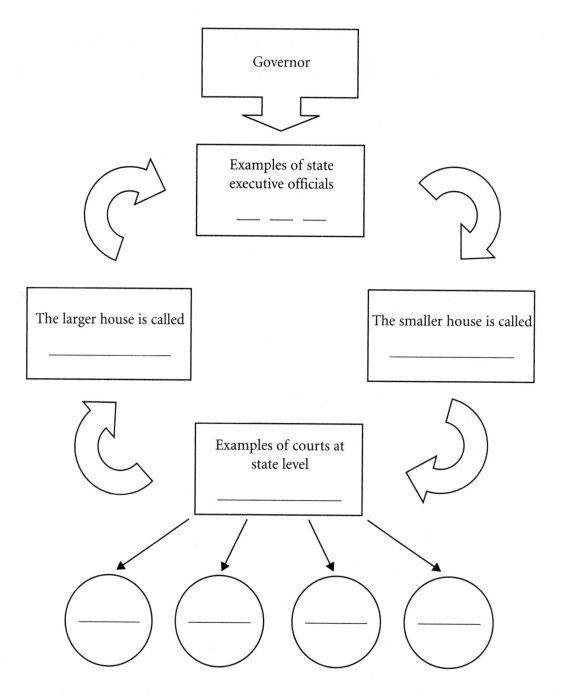

Chapter 1

Matching
1. i 6. g
2. f 7. a
3. e 8. d
4. h 9. c
5. j 10. b

Fill in the Blank
1. immigrant
2. native-born citizen
3. citizen
4. quotas
5. resources
6. metropolitan areas
7. Sunbelt
8. heritage

True/False
1. T 8. T
2. F 9. T
3. T 10. T
4. T 11. T
5. F 12. F
6. T 13. T
7. F 14. F

Identification
Answers appear in the following order:
c, e, d, b, a, f

Chapter 2

Matching
1. e 6. h
2. i 7. j
3. g 8. b
4. d 9. f
5. a 10. c

Fill in the Blank
1. laws 6. republic
2. Federalism 7. dictatorship
3. ratification 8. unitary system
4. totalitarian 9. Antifederalists
5. compromise

True/False
1. T 8. T
2. T 9. F
3. T 10. T
4. F 11. F
5. F 12. T
6. F 13. T
7. T 14. F

Identification
b, a, e, d, c

Chapter 3

Matching
1. c 6. j
2. g 7. d
3. i 8. h
4. e 9. b
5. a 10. f

Fill in the Blank
1. limited government
2. majority rule
3. delegated powers
4. Preamble
5. Popular sovereignty
6. reserved powers

True/False
1. F 8. F
2. T 9. T
3. T 10. F
4. F 11. T
5. T 12. T
6. F 13. F
7. F 14. F

Identification
legislative branch, makes laws;
executive branch, carries out laws;
judicial branch, interprets laws and punishes lawbreakers

Chapter 4

Matching

1. g	**6.** c
2. d	**7.** b
3. a	**8.** i
4. e	**9.** f
5. j	**10.** h

Fill in the Blank

1. separation of church and state
2. libel
3. self-incrimination
4. bail
5. poll tax
6. grand jury
7. petition
8. indicted

True/False

1. T	**7.** F
2. T	**8.** F
3. F	**9.** F
4. T	**10.** F
5. T	**11.** F
6. T	

Identification

1. guarantees freedom of religion, speech, and press
2. guarantees right to bear arms
3. Third
4. provides trial by jury in cases that involve conflicts over money or property
5. outlaws slavery
6. Fourteenth
7. African Americans are guaranteed the right to vote.
8. grants eligible voters in a state the right to elect the state's U.S. senators
9. Nineteenth
10. granted people of Washington, D.C., the right to vote
11. forbade poll tax
12. lowered voting age from 21 to 18

Unit 1

Matching

1. e	**7.** b
2. i	**8.** c
3. j	**9.** f
4. g	**10.** h
5. k	**11.** a
6. d	**12.** l

Fill in the Blank

1. totalitarian
2. delegated powers
3. native-born citizen
4. Antifederalists
5. republic
6. immigrant
7. limited government
8. self-incrimination
9. libel

True/False

1. F	**5.** F
2. T	**6.** F
3. T	**7.** T
4. T	**8.** T

Identification

d, b, e, c, a
Legislative branch—makes laws
Executive branch—carries out laws
Judicial branch—interprets laws and punishes lawbreakers

Chapter 5

Matching

1. f	**6.** a
2. e	**7.** i
3. c	**8.** g
4. h	**9.** j
5. b	**10.** d

Fill in the Blank

1. expulsion
2. franking privilege
3. immunity
4. term limit
5. censure
6. majority party
7. floor leader
8. apportioned

True/False

1. T
2. F
3. F
4. T
5. F
6. T
7. F
8. T
9. F
10. T
11. F

Identification

Senate—b, f
House of Representatives—a, e, g, h
both—c, d

Chapter 6

Matching

1. d
2. g
3. c
4. a
5. e
6. j
7. h
8. b
9. f
10. i

Fill in the Blank

1. pardon
2. consul
3. budget
4. executive departments
5. counterfeiting
6. ministers

True/False

1. F
2. F
3. T
4. F
5. T
6. F
7. T
8. F
9. T
10. T
11. T

Identification

b, d, f, g
a   h
c   j   e   i

Chapter 7

Matching

1. e
2. c
3. h
4. g
5. a
6. i
7. b
8. d
9. f
10. j

Fill in the Blank

1. hung jury
2. testimony
3. appeal
4. common
5. marshal
6. Territorial courts
7. court-martial

True/False

1. F
2. F
3. F
4. F
5. F
6. F
7. F
8. T
9. F
10. T
11. T
12. T
13. T
14. T

Identification

statutory law, d, g
b, a, CPSC example
f, based on rules, c
constitutional law, e

Unit 2

Matching

1. c
2. j
3. g
4. a
5. e
6. b
7. h
8. d
9. f
10. i

Fill in the Blank

1. franking privilege
2. appeal
3. immunity
4. term limit
5. apportioned
6. consul
7. ministers
8. executive departments
9. hung jury

True/False

1. T	**7.** T
2. T	**8.** F
3. F	**9.** F
4. T	**10.** T
5. T	**11.** F
6. T	

Identification

b, a

e, g

c, d, f

Chapter 8

Matching

1. c	**6.** g
2. f	**7.** j
3. d	**8.** b
4. i	**9.** e
5. a	**10.** h

Fill in the Blank

1. governor
2. Criminal cases
3. lieutenant governor
4. Civil cases
5. territories
6. complaint
7. justice of the peace

True/False

1. T	**7.** T
2. F	**8.** F
3. F	**9.** T
4. T	**10.** T
5. T	**11.** T
6. F	

Identification

b, e, g

c, i

a, d, f, h

Chapter 9

Matching

1. b	**6.** f
2. h	**7.** i
3. d	**8.** g
4. j	**9.** e
5. a	**10.** c

Fill in the Blank

1. ordinance
2. City council
3. wards
4. commission
5. county clerk
6. special district
7. district attorney
8. sheriff
9. county seat

True/False

1. T	**8.** F
2. F	**9.** F
3. T	**10.** F
4. T	**11.** F
5. F	**12.** F
6. T	**13.** F
7. T	**14.** F

Identification

a, e, b, d, c

Unit 3

Matching

1. f	**6.** a
2. i	**7.** e
3. c	**8.** j
4. h	**9.** d
5. g	**10.** b

Fill in the Blank

1. lieutenant governor
2. territories
3. straight ticket
4. presidential primaries
5. civil cases
6. popular vote
7. criminal cases
8. nominate

True/False

1. T	**7.** T
2. F	**8.** F
3. T	**9.** F
4. T	**10.** T
5. T	**11.** F
6. T	

Identification

c, b

f, e

a, d

Chapter 10

Matching
1. h	**6.** f
2. d	**7.** g
3. a	**8.** b
4. j	**9.** i
5. c	**10.** e

Fill in the Blank
1. popular vote
2. nominate
3. third-party
4. presidential primaries
5. straight ticket
6. favorite sons or daughters
7. multiparty system
8. primary election

True/False
1. F	**8.** F
2. T	**9.** T
3. T	**10.** F
4. T	**11.** F
5. F	**12.** T
6. T	**13.** T
7. F	**14.** T

Identification
a, c
e
b
d
f

Chapter 11

Matching
1. e	**6.** h
2. g	**7.** a
3. c	**8.** d
4. i	**9.** f
5. b	**10.** j

Fill in the Blank
1. Revealed propaganda
2. bandwagon
3. Concealed propaganda
4. Name-calling
5. Public opinion
6. Testimonial

7. mass media
8. plain-folks appeal
9. poll

True/False
1. F	**8.** F
2. F	**9.** T
3. T	**10.** T
4. T	**11.** F
5. F	**12.** T
6. F	**13.** F
7. F	**14.** F

Identification
1. a	**4.** b
2. c	**5.** e
3. d	

Chapter 12

Matching
1. i	**6.** b
2. f	**7.** j
3. c	**8.** h
4. e	**9.** d
5. a	**10.** g

Fill in the Blank
1. Interest
2. real property
3. fees
4. fines
5. personal property
6. bond
7. deductions
8. Profit
9. exemption

True/False
1. F	**8.** T
2. F	**9.** F
3. F	**10.** T
4. T	**11.** F
5. F	**12.** T
6. F	**13.** T
7. T	**14.** T

Identification
b, c
a, d
e

Unit 4

Matching
1. f
2. h
3. c
4. b
5. d
6. a
7. e
8. i
9. j
10. g

Fill in the Blank
1. personal property
2. Interest
3. City council
4. special district
5. bond
6. Revealed propaganda
7. county clerk
8. Public opinion

True/False
1. F
2. F
3. T
4. F
5. F
6. T
7. T
8. F
9. T
10. F
11. T

Identification
1. d
2. b
3. g
4. f
5. a
6. h
7. c
8. e

Chapter 13

Matching
1. h
2. e
3. j
4. b
5. g
6. a
7. d
8. c
9. i
10. f

Fill in the Blank
1. compromises
2. two-income family
3. single-parent families
4. Blended families
5. delayed marriage

True/False
1. T
2. T
3. F
4. T
5. F
6. F
7. T
8. T
9. T
10. T
11. T
12. F
13. T
14. F

Identification
trends—a, d, e
problems—c, f
family expenses—b, g, h

Chapter 14

Matching
1. f
2. i
3. g
4. b
5. a
6. c
7. h
8. e
9. j
10. d

Fill in the Blank
1. creativity
2. prejudice
3. conditioning
4. community colleges
5. university
6. extracurricular activities

True/False
1. F
2. T
3. F
4. T
5. T
6. F
7. T
8. T
9. T
10. T
11. T

Identification
Types—e, h, b, g, c
Ages/Grades—a, j, f, d, i

Chapter 15

Matching
1. b
2. e
3. f
4. a
5. d
6. c

Fill in the Blank
1. crossroads
2. Suburbs
3. compulsory
4. communication
5. metropolitan area
6. recreation
7. volunteer groups
8. megalopolis

True/False
1. F	8. T
2. T	9. T
3. F	10. F
4. T	11. T
5. T	12. T
6. F	13. F
7. T	14. T

Identification
d, g
b, i
f, c
h, e
a, j

Chapter 16

Matching
1. g	6. a
2. i	7. h
3. b	8. f
4. j	9. c
5. e	10. d

Fill in the Blank
1. defense
2. criminal justice system
3. probable cause
4. community policing
5. plea bargain
6. arraigned
7. parole
8. acquitted

True/False
1. F	8. F
2. F	9. T
3. T	10. F
4. T	11. F
5. F	12. F
6. T	13. F
7. T	14. T

Identification
Police officers—c, f
Criminals—a, d
Juvenile delinquents—b, e

Unit 5

Matching
1. g	6. e
2. c	7. h
3. a	8. d
4. b	9. i
5. j	10. f

Fill in the Blank
1. recreation
2. crossroads
3. two-income family
4. Motivation
5. delayed marriage
6. probable cause
7. community colleges
8. community policing

True/False
1. T	8. F
2. T	9. T
3. T	10. T
4. F	11. T
5. T	12. F
6. T	13. F
7. T	14. F

Identification
Problems—Effects:
b, e
a, d
f, c

Chapter 17

Matching
1. g	6. f
2. j	7. b
3. e	8. i
4. c	9. d
5. h	10. a

Fill in the Blank
1. law of demand
2. dividends
3. market economy
4. nonprofit organizations

5. corporation
6. stockholders
7. monopoly
8. invest
9. free competition

True/False

1. F	**7.** T
2. F	**8.** F
3. T	**9.** T
4. F	**10.** T
5. T	**11.** T
6. T	

Identification

d, b, g, a, f, e, c

Chapter 18

Matching

1. c	**6.** h
2. b	**7.** f
3. e	**8.** g
4. j	**9.** d
5. a	**10.** i

Fill in the Blank

1. division of labor
2. Machine tools
3. Self-service
4. Advertising
5. Standard packaging
6. assembly line
7. Interchangeable parts

True/False

1. F	**7.** F
2. F	**8.** T
3. T	**9.** T
4. F	**10.** T
5. T	**11.** F
6. T	

Identification

a, d, g
b, c, f
h, e, i

Chapter 19

Matching

1. d	**6.** i
2. h	**7.** b
3. a	**8.** g
4. j	**9.** c
5. f	**10.** e

Fill in the Blank

1. Private insurance
2. creditors
3. check
4. social insurance
5. Money market funds
6. short-term credit
7. Certificates of deposit
8. Long-term credit
9. Mutual funds

True/False

1. F	**7.** F
2. T	**8.** T
3. T	**9.** T
4. F	**10.** T
5. T	**11.** F
6. F	

Identification

Spend—a, d, g
Save—b
C—stocks, e, f

Chapter 20

Matching

1. h	**6.** c
2. f	**7.** i
3. b	**8.** g
4. j	**9.** a
5. e	**10.** d

Fill in the Blank

1. labor unions
2. Lockouts
3. costs of production
4. contraction
5. Blacklists
6. job action
7. collective bargaining
8. Inflation
9. trough

True/False

1. T	**7.** T
2. F	**8.** F
3. F	**9.** F
4. T	**10.** T
5. T	**11.** F
6. F	

Identification

Expansion—a, d, e, g
Contraction—b, c, f

Chapter 21

Matching

1. i	**6.** j
2. g	**7.** e
3. d	**8.** b
4. h	**9.** f
5. a	**10.** c

Fill in the Blank

1. circular-flow model
2. comparative advantage
3. producer
4. trade barrier
5. Supply
6. tax incentive
7. Opportunity cost
8. easy-money policy
9. Open-market operations

True/False

1. F	**8.** F
2. F	**9.** F
3. F	**10.** F
4. T	**11.** F
5. F	**12.** F
6. F	**13.** F
7. T	**14.** T

Identification

Fed lowers discount rate, b
d, economy slows
easy-money policy enacted, b
government raises taxes, c
a, economy expands

Chapter 22

Matching

1. j	**6.** b
2. f	**7.** g
3. a	**8.** c
4. h	**9.** e
5. d	**10.** i

Fill in the Blank

1. operators
2. Interpersonal skills
3. Automation
4. laborers
5. Agribusinesses
6. aptitude tests

True/False

1. T	**8.** T
2. F	**9.** T
3. F	**10.** F
4. T	**11.** F
5. F	**12.** F
6. F	**13.** T
7. F	**14.** T

Identification

White-collar workers—d, f
Blue-collar workers (e)—b, h
Service workers—a, c
Agricultural workers—g

Unit 6

Matching

1. h	**6.** i
2. e	**7.** b
3. j	**8.** g
4. c	**9.** f
5. a	**10.** d

Fill in the Blank

1. Certificates of deposit
2. market economy
3. Advertising
4. creditors
5. Inflation
6. Competition
7. Agribusinesses

True/False

1. T	**8.** T
2. T	**9.** F
3. T	**10.** F
4. F	**11.** T
5. T	**12.** T
6. F	**13.** T
7. F	**14.** T

Identification

Contraction—b, c, f
Expansion—a, d, e, g

Chapter 23

Matching

1. c	**6.** b
2. i	**7.** g
3. j	**8.** e
4. a	**9.** d
5. f	**10.** h

Fill in the Blank

1. Free trade
2. diplomatic corps
3. Imports
4. Couriers
5. Exports
6. International Court of Justice
7. Trade deficits
8. Diplomatic recognition

True/False

1. T	**8.** F
2. F	**9.** T
3. T	**10.** T
4. T	**11.** F
5. F	**12.** T
6. F	**13.** F
7. T	**14.** F

Identification

NATO—b, e
f, North American Free Trade Agreement, d
UN—a, c

Chapter 24

Matching

1. h	**6.** g
2. b	**7.** j
3. e	**8.** f
4. a	**9.** c
5. d	**10.** i

Fill in the Blank

1. Satellite nations
2. corollary
3. balance of power
4. Perestroika
5. neutrality
6. terrorists
7. glasnost
8. doctrine
9. limited war

True/False

1. F	**7.** F
2. T	**8.** T
3. T	**9.** T
4. T	**10.** F
5. F	**11.** F
6. T	

Identification

c, f, e, a, b, g, d

Unit 7

Matching

1. d	**6.** g
2. i	**7.** b
3. c	**8.** f
4. a	**9.** j
5. h	**10.** e

Fill in the Blank

1. Exports
2. doctrine
3. Free trade
4. balance of power
5. Diplomatic recognition
6. diplomatic corps
7. Imports
8. Perestroika
9. neutrality

True/False

1. F 　　 7. T
2. F 　　 8. T
3. T 　　 9. T
4. T 　　 10. F
5. T 　　 11. T
6. F

Identification

statutory law, d, g
b, a, CPSC example
f, based on rules, c
constitutional law, e

Chapter 25

Matching

1. h 　　 6. g
2. a 　　 7. c
3. f 　　 8. j
4. d 　　 9. e
5. b 　　 10. i

Fill in the Blank

1. Dissent
2. Building codes
3. demonstration
4. boycott
5. civil disobedience
6. Zoning laws
7. Mass transit

True/False

1. F 　　 7. T
2. T 　　 8. F
3. F 　　 9. T
4. F 　　 10. T
5. F 　　 11. T
6. F

Identification

b, d, c, a, e

Chapter 26

Matching

1. b 　　 6. c
2. g 　　 7. f
3. j 　　 8. h
4. a 　　 9. i
5. d 　　 10. e

Fill in the Blank

1. smog
2. Landfills
3. Pesticides
4. Desertification
5. Acid rain
6. Erosion
7. Recycling
8. Organic farming
9. ecosystem

True/False

1. F 　　 8. T
2. T 　　 9. F
3. F 　　 10. F
4. F 　　 11. T
5. T 　　 12. F
6. F 　　 13. F
7. F 　　 14. T

Identification

1. b 　　 4. a
2. d 　　 5. c
3. e

Unit 8

Matching

1. g 　　 6. h
2. j 　　 7. f
3. d 　　 8. b
4. i 　　 9. c
5. a 　　 10. e

Fill in the Blank

1. Zoning laws
2. smog
3. Recycling
4. civil disobedience
5. Acid rain
6. Landfills
7. Building codes
8. boycott
9. Dissent

True/False

1. F	**7.** T
2. T	**8.** T
3. F	**9.** T
4. F	**10.** F
5. F	**11.** F
6. T	

Identification

Graph #1: b, d, f

Graph #2: a, c, e, g